I. M. Levitt
Dandridge M. Cole

EXPLORING
THE SECRETS
OF SPACE

Astronautics
for the Layman

PRENTICE-HALL, INC.   *Englewood Cliffs, N. J.*

629.4
L 666

Exploring the Secrets of Space:
Astronautics for the Layman
by I. M. Levitt and Dandridge F. Cole

Library of Congress Catalog Card Number: 63-9838

Printed in the United States of America
29747-T

Prentice-Hall International, Inc.
London • Tokyo • Sydney • Paris

Prentice-Hall of Canada, Ltd.

Prentice-Hall de Mexico, S.A.

Acknowledgments

THE AUTHORS wish to acknowledge their debt to many people and organizations who have contributed to bringing this work to fruition. We are indebted to the various observatories for making available their unexcelled photographs to be used as illustrations. We are indebted to Martin M. Decker, President of the Decker Corporation of Bala Cynwyd, Pa., for making available the illustrations which are used to accompany much of the text. We owe thanks to the Editors of the *Philadelphia Inquirer* for it was on their insistence that many of the illustrations were first drawn for use in a superbly produced Sunday Supplement. Very kindly, the General Features Corporation of New York permitted the use of the artwork which illustrates a column written by one of the authors. Last, we would like to acknowledge our gratitude to Dr. Roy K. Marshall for a definitive reading of the astronomical portions of the book and his wise counsel in editing.

The Scope
of This Book

BEFORE THE launching of Sputnik I on October 4, 1957, books on astronautics were few and far between. A student of the field could easily read all that were published and, in fact, had difficulty finding enough material to satisfy his thirst for knowledge.

Now, with scores of satellites in operation, manned orbital flights, and plans underway for a manned trip to the moon, more books are being published on astronautics than any single individual can possibly absorb. The professional or amateur astronautical scientist must be very discriminating in his choice of reading material.

What of the newcomer to the field? Where should he begin? The array of titles is bewildering, even to the expert. The new student may easily be confused, and possibly discouraged, by selecting a book which is too difficult or perhaps too elementary. Some books which include the word "elementary" in their titles require a full college science and mathematical program as prerequisites to understanding their content. Others, which claim to contain all there is to know about a subject, are aimed at pre-high school levels of education.

It is hoped that this book will prove to be intermediate in difficulty and in comprehensive coverage of the subject. It will probably prove too difficult for those without any high school science or mathematics, and yet it does not require that the reader be a science or mathematics major. The very few places in which more than a high school level of mathematics is employed can be skipped without serious loss.

Through necessity, almost all recent books on astronautics introduce the reader to some knowledge of astronomy. Many modern astronomy texts add a chapter on space travel to stimulate reader interest. However, none combine astronomy and astronautics in a single volume in what the present authors believe to be a reasonable division of emphasis.

The future space traveler, or student astronaut, should have a good foundation in the "geography" of the solar system and general astronomy in order to understand the objectives of astronautics. A surprisingly high percentage of those actively working in the missile and space vehicle fields know almost nothing about astronomy. We have, therefore, devoted approximately one-half of this volume to the fundamentals of astronomy and wish that even more pages could be spared for the oldest and purest of the sciences.

Another departure from the typical book on space travel is our emphasis on fundamental scientific concepts—the laws of motion, systems of units, significant figures, etc. Again we have found many engineers and scientists actively engaged in space flight programs who badly need review of these fundamentals.

In the astronautics sections, we have emphasized propulsion and general booster design concepts. It is these areas of space flight engineering that represent the "bottleneck" and the "stumbling blocks" to the attainment of large-scale, economic space flight and have retarded the realization of any space accomplishments until now.

Problems of guidance and control, re-entry, aerodynamic flight, space biology, etc., although difficult and sometimes highly complex, can usually be solved during the development cycle of the new, large, booster engine and propulsion system. While we may be criticized for omitting discussion of some of these important areas, we believe our selection of astronomy, propulsion, fundamental mechanics, booster conceptual design, staging, and space flight missions, will prove most useful to the beginning student or the interested layman.

A number of new concepts are presented here for the first time in this form. These include "The Panama Theory of Strategic Areas in Space," the concept of Macro-life, encapsulated symbiotic life, the contained nuclear explosion propulsion system, etc. Because of these new concepts, the review of fundamental mechanics, and the wealth of astronomical information, we believe this book may be of interest to the professional, as well as the student and layman.

If this book can help in some small way to convince the reader that our national space program is essential and merits support, or if it can aid in the education of any who will build or fly the rockets to the moon and the planets, we will be well satisfied with our efforts.

Contents

CHAPTER 1

Why Go Into Space?

L ETTERS APPEAR IN the editorial pages of papers across the country from laymen asking pertinent questions of our time: "Why are we going into space? What good is it? What will it mean to me or my children?"

These letters are written by people in all walks of life. Some of the writers are highly educated: they may be doctors, students, clergymen, businessmen or housewives.

Our space scientists have been asked these questions frequently. Some of the questioners are the Congressmen who are responsible for the allocation of funds going into our space program, while others are businessmen trying to predict how the program will affect their own little empires. Congressmen have stated that, but for the wave of popular interest in space following the John Glenn flight, it would have been necessary to cut space funds drastically.

In an attempt to answer these questions and view them in their proper perspective, let's talk about money.

It has been estimated that the National Aeronautics and Space Administration will spend from $50 to $70 billion on peaceful, scientific space programs by 1970. The Department of Defense may reach the same level of spending on the military aspects of space. The total will exceed $12 billion a year for this period. We must assume that the Russians are spending a comparable sum of money. Thus we know that the world-wide space effort may approach $20 billion a year. In ten years—say shortly after the end of this decade—the total cost will exceed $200 billion.

Consider what $200 billion can do in the way of schools, hospitals, housing, etc. This sum is so staggering that it is almost impossible to visualize the results of its expenditure. However, if you think we are the only ones guilty of such thinking, the citizenry of Russia is also puzzled by the new Soviet penchant for space travel. The following paragraph appeared in an Associated Press dispatch datelined Moscow, June 12, 1960:

'What do sputniks give to a person like me?' a Russian workman complained in a letter which Pravda published on its front page. 'So much money is spent on sputniks it makes people gasp. If there were no sputniks, the government could cut the cost of cloth for an overcoat and put a few electric flatirons in the stores. Rockets, rockets, rockets! Who needs them now?'

Perhaps all taxpayers are alike in that they want to know—and they are entitled to know—"What good is space travel?"

Whenever an occasion arises where huge sums of money are spent, we hear the question raised as to the ultimate end to which this money is put. It is asked every time there is a major war. Although it is difficult to justify war except as a means of national survival, certain benefits do accrue as a result of wars, and the benefits from space travel can be even greater.

National security values, for example, hold genuine significance to this country in several ways. One benefit results from the uses to which our armed forces can put knowledge gained from space exploration. The second results from the influence and prestige that America can exert within the world community because of her prowess in space exploration. A third results from the possibility that space exploration, eventually, may prove so immense and important a challenge that it will channel the prime energies of powerful nations toward this end and reduce the current emphasis on developing means of destruction.

Another possibility which cannot be ignored is that an unfriendly country will develop new space weapons that directly threaten our security, or that we will develop new space weapons which improve our defenses. Finally, there is the possibility that strategic areas (comparable to the Panama Canal) exist in space which may have great military or commercial significance in the long-range competition between East and West.

The first two values definitely exist. The third seems to be a reasonable aspiration, while we hope that international cooperation and disarmament can eliminate the others. However, we would like to stress only better living and better health. These are items recognized even by those most hostile to space travel.

CONSUMER BY-PRODUCTS OF SPACE

A few years ago, there was a need for power in space and a need for temperature control. How would the scientist fulfill this need? Scientists went back more than 125 years to uncover an almost forgotten discovery to provide power and temperature control. About 125 years ago, an Estonian scientist, Thomas Seebeck, discovered that when two strips of metal of different composition were soldered together and the junction heated, a tiny electric current was generated. Shortly 'thereafter, the French scientist Jean Peltier discovered that heat is absorbed or liberated at the junction of two dissimilar metals carrying an electric current. This became known as the *Peltier effect*.

When space scientists began worrying about cooling or heating in space, they knew that whatever scheme was devised, if it took energy to operate it, this energy was available, because in space the sun was ever present. The trick was how to use that power to cool or warm a space capsule. To do this, they called upon the effect discovered more than a century ago, the Peltier effect. We can surmise that when the space ships begin circling the earth, the Peltier effect will be used to cool or heat them.

Today we find small refrigerators and air conditioning units on the market without a single moving part. If the current is reversed, this device may also be used to heat our homes. In the next ten years, the thing we may have most of and that may cost least is energy and, given sufficient energy, we can use this novel, trouble-free type of refrigeration or heating.

We know that water shortage will be a problem of the future. Scientists tell us that in another ten years the water situation will become critical.

Part of the space program deals with the use and reuse of water in the closed environment of a space ship. It is conceivable that one significant result of the research going into this program will be the knowledge of how to use our present water supply to maximum advantage. The ability of the scientist to find ways to reuse water may eventually permit him to tackle the staggering problem of distilling fresh water from sea water. Whether we like it or not, it may be that within ten years we will be using water that has come from the sea in large quantities.

COMMUNICATIONS

There is a large balloon-like satellite in the sky called ECHO I which has been used as a passive communications satellite. Messages and television pictures have been bounced off it from coast to coast. Again, the average individual will say, "So what?" So, we have a communications satellite in the sky! The truth of the matter is that we can not ignore a serious situation which could ultimately result in a communications breakdown in the world. Already the overseas lines are completely overburdened and many attempts at trans-Atlantic communication have ceased because of the inability to get through. The cables and radio telephony circuits are overcrowded. The only solution lies in a complex of active communications satellites which will permit messages to be transmitted with complete assurance that they will get through.

Active satellites can increase communications capabilities significantly.

So far only voice communications have been mentioned. Engineers think of communication in terms of channels. They tell us there are less than 100 telephone channels across the Atlantic. A single television channel is equivalent in band width to 1000 telephone channels. Thus television regularly transmitted over cables is completely out of the question. But with a satellite the shortcomings disappear. The Telstar communications satellite can transmit television, and there is no end to its capabilities. When the synchronous active satellites are in orbit at 22,300 miles above the earth's surface, we will realize global television.

Perhaps these arguments will leave the average reader a trifle cold. Let's talk about something which will more likely affect his pocketbook—his most vulnerable spot.

WEATHER SATELLITES

Mark Twain's editor and colleague, Charles Dudley Warner, once said "Everyone talks about the weather, but nobody does anything about it." Although this has been true in the past, with the future will come the means for understanding and, perhaps, modifying the weather.

Many TIROS weather satellites are in the sky. These satellites are transmitting television pictures of weather patterns to the surface of the earth. Eventually TIROS will give way to the earth-oriented NIMBUS satellite and, finally, to AEROS, which will be a synchronous satellite reporting weather from an altitude of 22,300 miles.

Some satellites are measuring the influx of solar energy. Others are measuring the amount and distribution of the energy reflected back into space. They are televising patterns, evolution and motions of clouds and transmitting them to the earth. They are also pin-pointing potentially dangerous storms. The result of these satellites will be that the weatherman will have a much better understanding of the weather and his forecasts will be more accurate.

Today, there are weather stations monitoring 20% of the earth's surface. Eighty per cent of the earth's surface is devoid of weather stations. This is understandable because oceans cover 70% of the earth's surface. Yet, despite this fact, laymen expect the weatherman to predict weather with an accuracy of 100%, It simply can not be done at this time.

With the advent of the operational weather satellites, continuous monitoring of the weather from high altitudes will enable the weatherman to watch storms, hurricanes and tornadoes develop and warn of their arrival. It is estimated that a half billion dollars would be saved by the farmer and businessman if we could improve our weather forecasts by only 10%. No longer will there be unpredicted flash frosts in Florida to wreak havoc with the citrus crop and, subsequently, with pocketbooks the following season when orange juice is in short supply.

TECHNOLOGICAL AND SCIENTIFIC BENEFITS

The necessity of working with exotic materials to fulfill the demands of our space technology has revealed new and potentially valuable processes. A new, high-powered, electron beam gun has been developed for welding the most refractory metals. It has been used successfully on molybdenum and tungsten, and the welds have proved not only satisfactory but superior in performance.

The fantastic cutting action of a rocket engine has been successfully used in quarrying and mining operations. Uneconomical taconite has been mined by jet drilling which has opened up vast iron resources in this country. Without the new method of drilling, it would be impossible to work the taconite fields.

A device like an old-time shutter has been developed to regulate the temperature in capsules. A logical follow-on to this could be used to automatically regulate the temperature in our homes; the entire process could be an automatic one controlled by a thermostat.

Mapping of the earth has been high on the list of scientific tasks for geodesists. A flashing geodetic satellite photographed against a stellar background can yield positions with an accuracy of about 50 feet. This type of accuracy will permit scientists to test the continental drift theory without having to wait literally for centuries so that the distances will be measurable.

Space is an almost perfect vacuum. Once man is in space, this vacuum is available for his experiments. On the earth there is an entire industry devoted to producing a vacuum which is, at best, an imperfect vacuum. Although this multi-million dollar industry will not be destroyed because of its need on earth, the attempts to improve vacuum techniques may not be pursued. Experiments involving fusion may take on new significance because of the availability of a perfect vacuum.

In detailing the scientific and technological benefits that will accrue to mankind, it may be noted that we now possess a permanent housepaint. We are using pyroceram pots and pans that can go directly from the freezer to the oven. The miniaturization in electronics is reflected in our radios which can now be made in the size of a lump of sugar. These can be powered with the same solar cells that power active satellites orbiting the earth. New electrostatic cameras developed for satellites can produce instant movies or still pictures with no processing.

HEALTH IN THE FUTURE

We are all aware that one of the most serious handicaps to manned space flight is the completely alien and unfriendly environment of space. In space we find radiations ranging from the highly energetic cosmic rays, gamma rays, X rays and ultraviolet radiation down to the longwave radio waves. Most of these highly energetic radiations are lethal. In space there are chunks of rock which whiz by at a speed 90 times that of a rifle bullet. Also, in space, without the protective atmosphere, there are severe temperature changes. We all recognize that these elements are not conducive to the well-being of man.

How do we get around this hostile environment? In the past, scientists have always said that we cannot change man, so we must adapt the machine to fit man. This saying may become obsolete. Some scientists have suggested that the study of possible changes which man might temporarily effect in his body chemistry and body physics may bring about a more certain compatibility between himself and space.

Active studies are being pursued aiming to change the human being with psychological, pharmacological and physiological inputs to permit him to acclimate himself to space. Although very little work is being done in the physiological field, some scientists suggest this as a fertile field for study.

Basically and theoretically, there are three tactics available to assure man's survival in space.

The first, and the one being actively pursued by both the Russians and the Americans, is a simple one: That we simply bring our environment along with us, as in the Mercury capsule. There is a long history for this. Divers have labored under water in caissons which permit them to work without diving suits. Aviators, and indeed, jet passengers travel in pressurized cabins that provide a surface environment. However, in the case of the astronauts, there is a tremendous penalty involved: Everything needed in space must be brought up from the earth.

The second tactic involves the transformation of a hostile environment to a benign one. This tactic is also being actively pursued by many countries. Some countries, like Israel, will go to the desert and, given sufficient power, will be able to drill for water, irrigate, air condition and, perhaps, even modify the weather. They can not only make the desert bloom; they can synthesize chemicals and materials needed for life.

The third tactic involves the use of mutants or biologically abnormal individuals. Under certain conditions, the normal individual will be unable to survive. But, because of the abnormality of mutants, they can survive serious environmental changes. This is an evolutionary tactic and is impractical because of the inordinately long time scale involved.

However, we have a basic principle working for us. This principle states that, if a mechanism is known, there can always be found a way to modify it in a desired direction.

As an example of this, we know that when the temperature of the body drops below 60°F. we can not survive. The question is:

What is the mechanism that causes death? Is it perhaps a coagulation of the blood at low temperatures which affects the vital organs? Perhaps the blood demulsifies. If the mechanism can be discovered, a decoagulant may be added to the blood or an emulsion stabilizer added. In this way the scientist will have interfered with the normal process, the end of which is death.

This novel idea can be illustrated by another example. In World War II a pill was developed for stranded soldiers which permitted them, for a few hours after eating, to digest and derive energy from grass, leaves, bark—all normally indigestible cellulose. It is well known that human beings cannot digest these plants because we do not possess the proper chemical or enzyme to process grass. Cows and certain other mammals do possess this enzyme. Thus, a pill containing the proper enzyme from these animals, when taken by a man, enabled him to exist by deriving energy from cellulose.

Another approach to the problem of living in space is the creation of *Cyborgs*—meaning cybernetic organisms. In this concept, space men will have devices deliberately incorporated into them to extend the unconscious self-regulatory control, thus permitting adaptation to the environment.

As an example, consider the case where blood pressure is important. An instrumented capsule containing the proper drugs can be placed inside the body. The capsule will sense the blood pressure dependent on space conditions, compare it to a reference value and re-establish the correct blood pressure by administering a proper dose of a drug. This will be a wholly automatic operation in which the human being will be the interested but passive bystander.

Consider the case of a solar flare in which the radiation level were increased perhaps 100,000 times. In this case, the man in space may have built into him another instrument which can sense the radiation level and automatically inject into the bloodstream the drug necessary to ward off the effects of the increased radiations. Again the operation would be automatic without the astronaut being aware of what had taken place.

During prolonged flights there will be little for the astronaut to see or do. A practical solution to this problem will be to have the astronaut sleep for, say, 23 out of the 24 hours. This can be done with drugs or with an electrical device that induces sleep by the passage of an electric current through the brain. The Russians have built a device called an *Electroson* that does just this.

The control device governing sleep and wakefulness could be preset to arouse the astronaut in an emergency.

Even pleasurable sensations might be stimulated in the case of long trips. One intriguing pharmacological possibility is the recent work done on the "pleasure center" of the brain. It is thought that periodic stimulation of this area may provide a "satisfaction" to relieve the monotony and anxieties of space flight. An unforeseen accident yielding pain and suffering is always a possibility. Under these circumstances the astronaut would be able to select a state of unconsciousness with prolonged sleep induced either by drugs or electronics.

At the Douglas Aircraft Company, they have developed *mini-sensors* to measure the physical and psychological responses of jet pilots which, in turn, they hope will point the way to monitoring the reactions of astronauts. Employing the latest electronic microminiaturization techniques, they have developed an instrument about the size of a nickel which, when secured directly to a pilot's chest, automatically broadcasts heart data to a radio receiver 50 feet away.

Although acquiring the information is not difficult, processing the data represents a bottleneck. The use of high-speed computers could materially help the study. Toward this end a *heart machine* has been developed which reports instantly, on a panel display, whether a subject has a normal heartbeat or is a victim of one of four major cardiac disorders. The machine listens to the heart beat and compares the sound of a subject's heart with the sound of normal and abnormal heart sounds. There are startling overtones in this concept for it may find use in forestalling heart attacks.

Space-medicine doctors have not stopped here. They have actually implanted tiny instruments inside the bodies of small monkeys to monitor certain physiological functions.

In one case, doctors inserted, inside a monkey, a small device for transmitting a radio signal to a receiver outside the body to relay information concerning the behavior of the heart. The tiny instrument must be powered, so small batteries inside the monkey were irradiated by radio energy for this power. This proved highly successful.

Scientists are now hoping to expand this concept and, along with cardiograms, they visualize a flowmeter implanted in the aorta which could measure blood flow under certain conditions. They also visualize a device which would monitor kidney function by measuring ureteral flow. The lungs and liver are two other organs susceptible to this treatment.

All of these developments will eventually give rise to automatic hospitals. These electronic "nurses" will relieve the ever-increasing shortage of hospital nurses and aides. In time a single nurse sitting in front of a complex of instruments and dials will monitor the physiological conditions of patients on an entire hospital floor.

Still other developments help us maintain our health and well-being. The intense pin-point of light of the LASER, which has an intensity a million times that of the sun, has been used for retinal welding, that is, for restoring the sight of an eye with a detached retina. The LASER has also been used to coagulate the blood in brain surgery.

The hearing of some deaf persons has been restored by the implant of tiny electronic devices.

Pressure suits developed for our astronauts make it possible for bedridden victims of strokes to walk, work and lead normal lives. These suits achieve their objective by restoring the necessary tone to the blood vessels to normalize the blood pressure.

Miniature television cameras, powered by batteries, have become smaller and smaller. Eventually they may be made tiny enough to be swallowed to transmit on-the-spot pictures of the stomach.

Other organs of the body may also be scrutinized with this equip-ment, permitting intimate physiological examinations.

All of these new devices, techniques and equipment will serve but one objective: The well-being of our society. Never before in the history of man has so much effort been expended towards achieving a goal. If events progress as scientists visualize them, the impact of these advances will leave a lasting mark on our civiliza-tion.

These are but some of the advances which go far in answering the question: "Why go into space?" Undoubtedly there are others, and only the very bold can foretell all the benefits to be gained in the future. Even if the advances which contribute so much to our welfare were to stop today, the price we have paid or will pay will be insignificant in comparison to the benefits to which our society is heir.

Yet these enormous benefits which we expect from the space program are merely by-products. It is legitimate to ask, "What results could be expected if all our space efforts were aimed directly at the products discussed here rather than at space flight?" Perhaps they would be even greater. Thus, we have not really answered the question of why it is urgent to go into space. Although scientists can tell us many things they would like to learn out there, "What is the hurry?" The only answer to that, the only reason for urgency and the rapid expenditure of enormous sums of money, is international competition.

There are at least three aspects to this competition that have already been mentioned briefly. One is national prestige, of which we have heard much since the launching of the first Sputnik on October 4, 1957. But true prestige would not be gained in a purely arbitrary contest. The contest must have real purpose of its own besides mere prestige.

The second and most important aspect of the competition is military. James Webb, Director of NASA, and Dr. Edward Welsh, Executive Secretary of the National Aeronautics and Space

Council, as well as many military leaders, have repeatedly stressed military competition as the main reason for urgency.

Consider, for example, just a few possibilities. It is possible that a space-based, anti-ICBM system could be developed that could almost completely eliminate an adversary's ICBM threat. Obviously, this could have serious, perhaps fatal, consequences if developed and deployed first by Russia.

The satellite bomber is another disturbing possibility. Russia is believed to have the lead in this development because of the greater payload capability of the Russian boosters. The satellite interceptor is of obvious importance because of the threat of the satellite bomber.

New weapons such as "death rays" developed from LASERS may be found to be more useful when operated from space bases. We are already in the era of the satellite "spy" or reconnaissance system. This alone can have tremendous effects on the balance of military power.

These are just a few of the space weapons systems we have already studied. There are more that have been studied and probably many more that have not yet been considered. It is this danger above all, that a space power could develop some entirely new and decisive space weapon system, that makes space development and space exploration an urgent necessity rather than a long-range, scientific research program.

One final aspect of space competition should be re-emphasized —the possible existence of strategic areas in space of importance comparable to that of the Panama Canal on earth. There is the danger that a competing power could gain a critical advantage through seizing and holding such areas.

In the long run, the taxpayer can expect to be paid back with interest for his investment in the space program through benefits to health, knowledge, weather prediction, communications, transportation, etc.; but these are not the things he is buying directly. What he is buying, and it is worth far more than he is paying, is the security and independence of his country.

CHAPTER 2

Distance and Time
In Astronautics

IN NO FIELD of science are the requirements for precise measure so exacting as in astronautics. Although some of the most accurately known numbers of all science are those of astronomy and astrophysics, they are still not known with sufficient precision for many of our current space flight projects.

If we should try to send an unmanned payload to the planet Mars with no correction of the trajectory after the initial boost period, we would almost certainly miss our target.* Even if the rocket operated with perfect accuracy and ended its thrust period with precisely the intended speed, in precisely the intended direction, at exactly the right place and time, it would still miss its target by many thousands of miles. While this may be difficult to believe, it is nevertheless true. The reason why it is true is that we do not know precisely how many miles away Mars is at any particular time, how fast it is moving or precisely how strong is the gravity of Mars, Earth or the sun. Although we know these numbers with greater accuracy than almost any numbers used in science, the accuracy is still not sufficient for the task, and a very

---

* Midcourse corrections were used for our Mariner 2 flight to Venus and the Soviet Mars probe.

small error in the aiming of our rocket can be a very large error after a flight of perhaps 300 million miles.

Part of our problem is that we have had no opportunity to make a direct comparison of the units of measurement that we use on earth with the units used in measuring in our solar system. We ordinarily measure our solar system with the *astronomical unit*— the average distance from the earth to the sun, which we will take for the time being as

$$9.2920 \times 10^7 \text{ miles}$$

Thus we know, for example, that Mars averages 1.524 astronomical units from the sun, Jupiter averages 5.203 and Pluto 39.457. These relative or comparative distances are known with high precision and enable us to predict the motions of the moon and the planets with great accuracy. There are no human predictions or prophecies which can be made with reliability and accuracy even approaching those with which astronomers predict future eclipses and other celestial events. The difficulty is that we do not know how many miles or kilometers there are in an astronomical unit nearly so accurately as we know, for example, the distance to Jupiter in astronomical units. Our artificial satellites and planetoids are beginning to give us better answers, however. By the time we are ready to land probes on the planets, our earlier planet-orbiting shots will have measured the inner solar system far more accurately than we could ever have done without these new scientific tools.

When we know the basic astronomical constants with sufficient accuracy, we will still not be able to hit Mars by shooting at it as a hunter does at a duck—allowing just enough lead to account for its velocity. Our present ability to control the position and velocity of a rocket is not that good. Rocket guidance and control experts say that an error of only one foot per second in the burn-out velocity of an ICBM is enough to cause a one-mile miss 5000 miles away. The rocket must have a burn-out velocity of 22,000 feet per second in order to go this distance, so that is an error of only one part in 22,000, or 0.0045%.

Some of our ICBM practice shots have come within less than a mile of their targets. This accuracy of one part in 5000 might be compared to hitting a one-foot target one mile away with a high powered rifle, or approximately a one-inch target at 500 feet!

Although this would be incredible accuracy for a rifle marksman, we must do much better in astronautics. A miss of one mile in 5000 would be 50 miles in 250,000—the approximate distance to the moon. This would not be serious, if our objective was just to hit the moon rather than a particular spot on the moon, but the story would be different if our target were Mars. At 50 million miles away, our tiny error of one foot in 5000 would grow to 10,000 miles, and we would miss the planet completely! *

Of course this "duck shooting" technique is not the only way to hit a target. If the space vehicle carries additional propellants, corrections can be made as needed. However, every pound of propellant used in this way represents a large increase in the cost of the project that could be saved by increased precision in the initial boost phase of the flight.

Precise measurement is one of the most fundamental functions of the scientist and engineer. Another basic scientific function, and one which is poorly understood, is prediction. More than anything else, the scientist is basically a prophet. Much as he may dislike the title, he has cast himself in that role.

A chemist can prophesy with great accuracy that Johnny is going to die if Johnny mistakes concentrated H_2SO_4 for H_2O and drinks a glassful; or if Johnny mixes several pounds of nitric acid and turpentine without taking extensive precautions. But perhaps we don't even need a chemist to tell us those things, and certainly no highly accurate measurements are needed.

A chemist could also tell us exactly when a glass of colorless

---

* Actually, even with this large error, our probe *might* be caught by the planet's gravity if not moving too fast; thus a hit might still be possible with the "duck shooting" method, although the probability of success would be low.

liquid would turn red as we gradually added a second colorless liquid in measured amounts. But he would have to know by precise measurement exactly how much acid was in the first glass (plus phenolphthalein indicator) and the exact concentration and rate of addition of the second hydroxide solution.

The physicist can prophesy very accurately concerning the impact of an artillery shell, the place, time, velocity, impact energy, etc.; but he must know just as accurately the condition of the shell as it leaves the muzzle. He must know the speed, angle, mass, etc.

As mentioned earlier, the astronomer can prophesy with very great accuracy the time of a future eclipse of the sun or moon, or the position of one of the planets of the solar system at some future date. But none of these prophecies can be better than the scientific knowledge about the conditions and behavior of the objects under study, which is gained through careful measurement.

UNITS OF MEASURE

In order to make accurate measurements we need units, or standards of comparison. Thus we have the familiar units of length, time, temperature, speed, etc. Those who have studied physics know also of the units of force and mass and may recall that physicists speak of fundamental units from which other units can be derived. In the branch of physics known as mechanics, the fundamental units are those of mass, distance or length, and time. From these can be derived units of force, energy, velocity, acceleration, impulse, area, volume, density and many others.

For example, a unit of distance divided by a unit of time gives a unit of speed or velocity. Thus we have miles per hour, kilometers per second, feet per second, etc. The only common units of velocity expressed in one word are the *knot,* or nautical mile per hour and the *Mach number.* A nautical mile is 6060 feet. Since it is equal to one minute of latitude, it is useful in navigation. The Mach number is useful in aeronautics but does not have much general application because it varies with environmental conditions. It is equal to the speed of sound; thus it depends on the temperature of the air. "Mach 2" refers to a velocity of twice the speed of sound.

Another unit of velocity which could become useful in astronautics as well as elsewhere in physics is the *stapp*.* One stapp equals 32.2 feet per second and is the velocity which a freely falling body will attain after falling for one second at sea level at 45° north latitude. This unit might be worth adding to the vocabulary of astronautics because of its value in simplifying certain basic concepts even though it is not now recognized as a physical unit.

The only unit of acceleration that has a name of its own has acquired this name through usage in aviation and astronautics. This is the *gee* (or g). This unit bears a close relationship to the stapp and serves a similar purpose.

One gee is the acceleration experienced by a freely falling body at sea level and 45° north latitude. It is equal to one stapp per second. Since the stapp is equal to 32.2 feet per second, the gee will contain the unit of time twice and will equal 32.2 feet per second per second, or 32.2 feet per second squared. When Colonel Stapp, "fastest man on earth," experienced a deceleration of 40 gees, his velocity was retarded at the rate of 40 stapps in each second, or a velocity change of 40 × 32.2 feet per second in each second. This is 1288 feet per second per second.

This velocity change can be expressed in miles per hour by multiplying by 3600 seconds per hour and dividing by 5280 feet per mile. It is worth remembering that this can also be done by dividing by the conversion factor, 1.47—($^{5280}/_{3600}$)—since this involves only one operation instead of two.

We find that Colonel Stapp's rate of deceleration was 880 miles per hour per second. This is equivalent to an object which is traveling at more than the speed of sound (760 miles per hour) coming to rest in one second!

---

* Named for Col. John P. Stapp, pioneer acceleration sled researcher responsible for our knowledge of human resistance to high accelerations.

UNITS OF LENGTH

The units of velocity discussed above were derived from units of length and units of time. The fundamental units of length are the foot or the yard in English units and the meter in metric units. For many years these fundamental units were defined as the lengths of platinum bars kept under carefully controlled conditions in London and Paris. Now, although the bars are still used as secondary references, the fundamental standard has been changed to the wave length of one of the spectral lines of the element mercury.

From the fundamental units, we derive the other familiar units of length such as the mile, the kilometer, etc. Of particular interest to astronautics are the astronomical unit, discussed earlier, the light-year and the parsec.

The *light-year* is commonly mistaken for a unit of time because the word "year" is used. However, it is actually equal to the enormous distance which light will travel in a year through the vacuum of interstellar space. Since light travels approximately 186,300 miles in a single second, we obviously do not have much use for light-years when measuring distances on earth. However, interstellar distances are so enormous that the nearest known star, Proxima Centauri, is 4.3 light-years away!

One light-year can be expressed in more familiar terms by multiplying the velocity of light by 3.156×10^7—the number of seconds in a year. The result is 5.88×10^{12} (5.8 trillion miles). A light-year is 63,310 astronomical units or approximately 31,655 times the diameter of the earth's orbit. If the radius of the earth's orbit—one astronomical unit—is represented by one inch, a light-year is approximately one mile. Also, we might note that the distance to the moon—250,000 miles in round numbers—is about 1.34 light-seconds, and the distance to the sun or the astronomical unit—92,920,000 miles—is about 500 light-seconds or 8.33 light-minutes.

UNITS OF TIME

Fortunately, there is not much confusion about the units of time. All systems use the same units—the second, minute, hour, day, etc.

The *second* (actually the *mean solar second*) is defined as one 86,400th part of a mean solar day. A *solar day* is the interval of time between two successive apparent noons. The *mean* solar day is the average length of the solar days in a year.

Unfortunately the spin rate of the earth is not an absolute constant. The earth is gradually slowing down because of the friction of the tides. Of course this change is very small, amounting to an increase in the length of the day of only one one-hundredth of a second in 1000 years. However, even such a small error as this cannot be tolerated in some precise astronomical work, so science has turned to a new clock that keeps even better time than the spinning earth. This is the orbital electron in the atom. Although there is no such thing as perfect accuracy, the atomic clock comes as close to perfection as anything yet measured by science.

SIGNIFICANT FIGURES

Although the need for high precision in astronautics which was emphasized earlier is generally understood, the related and equally important concept of significance or meaning in our scientific measurements is not so well understood. Millions of dollars are wasted every year because of lack of understanding of this basic principle among otherwise well-educated scientists and engineers.

The principle of significance states simply that *our results can never be more accurate than our original data.* Actually, the results will generally be less accurate because of inevitable errors and unnecessary confusing information which we introduce in our calculations. Engineers call this extraneous information "noise," by analogy with what occurs in vocal or radio communication.

Consider the children's game called "Whisper Down the Lane" in which a message is passed consecutively through a line of chil- 'dren. The message is always badly distorted by the time it gets to the end of the line. Noise in the room and "noise" in the children's brains add random and confusing extraneous information. Faulty reception causes the loss of some of the original information. The final form of the message cannot be better than the original and is usually much worse.

Suppose that we wish to measure the area of a rectangular plot of ground. We measure the width very accurately with a tape measure and find that it is 125.3 feet. However, we cannot measure the length at all accurately because of a stream running across the property (of course this would not represent much of a problem to a surveyor, but it happens that we do not want to get our feet wet). In any event, we make only a rough estimate of the length, which we realize could be incorrect by as much as two or three feet, and set down the length as 312 feet. (We should properly write it as 312 ± 3.) Now if we multiply the length by the width, we get 39,093.6 square feet. In the interest of accuracy, we might wish to retain the 0.6 square feet; however, it actually has no meaning: It is not a significant figure. In fact, the 9 and the 3 immediately preceding it are also without significance because we know the length only to three significant figures. The answer should be 39,100 square feet.

Suppose that a car travels a distance of 115.6 miles in a time estimated at 3.5 hours, and the average speed of the car is to be determined. In dividing the distance by the time, any desired number of decimal places could be computed. How far should the process be carried? As a simple, general rule we should remember to use no more figures in the answer than in the least accurate of our original numbers. Thus there should only be two significant figures in the answer which should be given as 33 miles per hour. If the time had been roughly estimated as "about three hours," the answer would be "about 30 miles per hour" with only a single significant figure. Note that significant figures have nothing to do with the position of the decimal point. A distance measured as 2.54 centimeters is 1.00 inches, 0.0254 meters and 0.0000254 kilometers. There are three significant figures in each case.

For a complete understanding of significant figures, a study must be made of the methods of calculating probable error. However, that will be left for courses in physics.

The most important point to remember is that the result cannot be more accurate than the least accurate of the input numbers. Since scientists and engineers pride themselves on their high precision, they are tempted to try to achieve accurate results even when it is not possible. Sometimes hundreds of inputs are used in solving modern problems of astronautics. If only one of these is a rough estimate, the answer may be equally rough. However, one rough estimate among hundreds of accurately known figures is sometimes ignored. The problem will be solved on a complex and costly computing machine and given the appearance of a highly accurate answer, when actually, considerable time and money could be saved by solving the problem within the accuracy of the estimated input by using a much simpler method.

The payload and velocity performance of a future rocket system can be estimated only approximately. It will not help us to improve the accuracy with which we calculate the payload it can carry to Mars by making very accurate calculations of the trajectory and the velocity requirements if we do not know, for example, whether we will use atmospheric braking or rocket braking in slowing down for a landing.

CHAPTER 3

Mass, Energy and Momentum In Astronautics

PROBABLY THE MOST difficult concept for the beginning student of physics to grasp is that of *mass*. This difficulty is more the result of sloppy habits of thought and careless use of words than of any intrinsic difficulty of the concept itself. All of us, including physicists and other scientists, frequently use the word weight when we mean mass.

Mass is sometimes defined as that property of matter which exhibits gravity and inertia. However, it is quite sufficient for our present purpose to say that the mass of an object is the quantity of matter or the amount of material in the object. The mass of an object does not depend on its position relative to the earth or other bodies, and it will normally remain unchanged unless some nuclear process (fission or fusion) takes place. The somewhat old-fashioned law of conservation of matter stated that matter (or mass) could not be created or destroyed. The total mass within a closed volume could not change, according to this law, regardless of what sort of reaction went on inside. We now know that mass can be converted into energy and vice versa. Therefore the law has been expanded to include both mass and energy. Thus, the total mass and energy in a closed volume must remain constant, regardless of what occurs within the volume.

The *weight* of an object, though often confused with its *mass,* is an entirely different thing. Weight is normally defined as the force of gravity acting on an object. However, in the space age we must note that. other forces can also produce the effect of weight. There is really nothing special about gravity in this respect.

The weight of an object is not a constant or intrinsic property of the object (as is mass). It is an effect resulting from the action of outside agencies. It will change as the object moves through the universe and may be zero in cases of free fall or in the absence of force fields.

The weight of an object would be different even in different parts of the earth. It will be slightly lower on high mountains than at sea level because the force of gravity decreases with increasing distance from the center of the earth. For the same reason it would be less at the equator than at the poles. It will also be less at the equator than at the poles because of the spin of the earth on its axis and the resulting centrifugal force.

An object in free space far from any other body would have zero weight—or almost zero. However, if this object were placed in the cabin of a space ship and the engines were turned on, the object would experience an effect almost indistinguishable from the weight normally caused by gravity.

If a space ship accelerated at a constant rate of one gee (one stapp per second), a passenger who had come into a closed compartment while on earth and slept until the ship had traveled far into space would have no way of knowing that he was no longer on earth. His weight would be the same. However, if the engines were then turned off, he would lose this synthetic but, nevertheless, real weight and become weightless. However, through this whole process his mass, or quantity of matter, would remain the same.

If the space ship passenger happened to be concerned about some excess fat on his body, he would be hardly less concerned in his weightless condition in space. The "overmass" person is usually concerned because excess fat is unhealthy and unsightly; difficulty in moving around is usually a secondary consideration. Although even a physicist may say that he is dieting to lose weight because he is too heavy, he really means that he wants to lose mass because he is too massive!

Units of mass and force are best discussed in connection with systems of units which will be done shortly. But first we should explore the concept of force.

Four fundamental forces are currently recognized by physicists. These are the *nuclear* force which holds the atomic nucleus together in spite of the powerful repulsive force between the subnuclear particles of like electrostatic charge, the *electrostatic* and *electrodynamic* (magnetic) forces which hold the molecules together, and the *gravitational* force which holds the solar system and the galaxy together. All other forces are believed to be derived from these four.

Some forces are called "fictitious" since they are considered to be merely reactions to the real forces. The weight of a book pushing down on the table is an example of the force of gravity. But the book would fall toward the ground if the table did not "push upward." This apparent activity of the table is an "unreal" reaction force. It does not actually push upward as it might appear. If the force of gravity suddenly ceased to exist, the table would not propel the book into space. Except for the spin of the earth which would send the book off horizontally (not vertically), the book would remain quietly on the table. The table no more than passively resists the imposed gravitational force.

When we tie a mass to the end of a string and whirl it around, the string exerts a real *centripetal* force on the mass which forces it to move in a circular path. The centripetal force is the result of the intermolecular, electrical forces holding the string together and our pull on the string (also basically electrical).

The *centrifugal* force does not pull outward on the string, as is sometimes said, it merely resists the inward pull of the string.

If the string is cut, the mass does not fly out on a radial course. It flies in a path tangent to the circle in the direction it was moving when the string parted.

Although there are only four forces known now, it would be well to remember that there were only four elements in the days of ancient Greece. Now there are over a hundred. Perhaps as our knowledge increases and our techniques for detecting and measuring forces improve, we may find that the four basic forces are not the only real, physical, dynamic agencies.

SYSTEMS OF UNITS

There are four so-called "rational" systems of units in common use, two English and two metric. The two first are the English Absolute System and the English Gravitational System. The metric systems are the CGS (centimeter, gram, second) system and the MKS (meter, kilogram, second) system. All of these are useful and logically consistent systems, although the two metric systems have some obvious advantages which will be discussed later.

Unfortunately there is a fifth system that is even more commonly used in the United States than the other four; it is sometimes given undeserved dignity by titling it the English Engineering System. The kindest way to describe it is to say that it is an "irrational" system and to add that it should not be used by rational scientists and engineers.

Systems of units can be clarified by noting their application to Newton's second law of motion which can be written $F = kma$, where f is force, m is mass, a is acceleration and k is a constant of proportionality. The law can then be stated in words, "When an object is accelerated by the application of an external force, the product of its mass and acceleration is directly proportional to the applied force."

This form of the second law can be used with any system of units or any combination of units just so long as we assign the proper value to k. However, scientists like to simplify their work as much as possible, so systems of units were devised—the rational systems

—such that k would equal one. Thus we can write the second law, $F = ma$, as long as we use "consistent" or "rational" units for the three quantities.

In the English Absolute System, the unit of mass is the *pound* which is defined as the mass of the standard platinum pound in England. If acceleration is expressed in feet per second, we can then use the second law to define the unit of force. One *poundal* is that quantity of force which will give a mass of one pound an acceleration of one foot per second squared.

The English Gravitational System uses the same units of length as the Absolute System but different units of mass and force. The unit of mass is the *slug,* and the unit of force is the pound. The slug can be defined as that quantity of mass which will experience an acceleration of one foot per second squared when acted on by one pound of force.

Although the one-pound mass will weigh approximately one pound anywhere on earth, its weight will decrease rapidly if it is moved off into space. At 4000 miles (one earth radius) it will drop to 0.25 pound, since we have doubled its distance from the center of the earth and the force of gravity decreases with the square of the distance. At 8000 miles from the surface and 12,000 miles from the center of the earth, its weight will be down to one-ninth of a pound. Although the force of the earth's gravity never drops quite to zero regardless of how far we go from the earth, it drops to less than the pull of the sun long before we reach the moon's orbit. At approximately one million miles away from the earth, an object can no longer stay in orbit about the earth because of the upsetting forces from distant celestial objects. Thus, one million miles can be considered the practical limit of the earth's gravitational field.

The metric systems are similar to each other and differ only in one major respect—the magnitude of the basic units. The MKS unit of mass is one thousand times the corresponding CGS unit.

The CGS unit of mass is the *gram,* which is defined as the mass of one cubic centimeter of water at 4 degrees centigrade and standard atmospheric pressure. The unit of force is the *dyne,* which is defined as the force which will accelerate a one-gram mass at a rate of one centimeter per second squared.

Unfortunately there is also a *gram of force* which is that force which will cause a gram of mass to accelerate at 980 centimeters per second squared. Since 980 centimeters per second squared is the acceleration of a falling body, it follows that a one gram mass will have a weight of one gram—at sea level at 45° north latitude.

The unit of mass in the MKS system is the *kilogram,* the unit of length is the *meter* and the unit of force is the *Newton.* One Newton is the force which will accelerate one kilogram at one meter per second squared.

Since a kilogram is 1000 grams, a Newton will accelerate 1000 grams at 100 centimeters per second squared and thus is equal to 100,000 dynes. A kilogram of force equals 9.8 Newtons.

WORK AND ENERGY

The words *work* and *energy* have very specific and definite meanings in science as contrasted with their ordinary use. We must be particularly careful that we understand the physical meaning of *work.* A man that exerts a force in pushing against a stalled car would normally be considered to be working even though he were not successful in moving the car. According to the scientific definition, however, the car must move before any work can be said to have been accomplished. In a somewhat over-simplified way, work can be defined as the product of force times the distance through which it is applied.

This definition of work is incomplete since it leaves out any mention of the direction of the force. In the branch of mathematics called *vector analysis,* this problem is handled systematically, and the force and distance—both defined as vectors, since they have both magnitude and direction—are combined according to specific rules. However, we can multiply a force and a distance safely and get accurate and correct values for the resulting work, so long as we remember that they must be in the same direction. If this is the case, the work done can easily be found by multiplying the force exerted by the distance through which it is exerted. Thus the units of work are a unit of force times a unit of distance. Any combination of force and distance units could be used, such as ton-parsecs, kilogram-miles, etc., but it is less confusing to use combinations from within a single system. Thus we commonly use foot-pounds, dyne-centimeters, foot-poundals, etc. A dyne-centimeter is given the special name *erg*.

Now suppose that the force and the resulting motion are not in the same direction. Consider the example of the child pulling a wagon or sled along a level road. The motion is horizontal but the force is at an angle to the horizontal—an inclined force along the rope or handle.

In such a case the force is divided into two parts, called *components*. We have a vertical and a horizontal component of the pull on the handle. The vertical component tends to lift the sled or wagon from the ground, while the horizontal component overcomes the friction of the wheels or runners and moves the object horizontally.

It can be shown that the vertical and horizontal components

Fig. 3-1 Components of force.

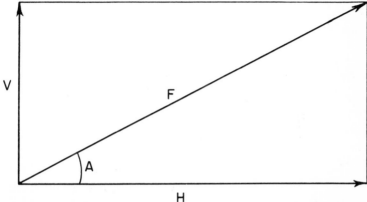

of the force are related to the force numerically in the same way that the sides of a rectangle are related to the diagonal. Thus the directed line segments of a rectangle can be used to represent the force vectors.

Let V and H represent the vertical and horizontal components of the force, F (Fig. 3.1). The directions of the lines represent the directions of the forces, and the lengths of the lines represent the magnitudes of the forces, that is, the number of kilograms or pounds.

From the Pythagorean theorem, $F^2 = V^2 + H^2$ and $H = \sqrt{F^2 - V^2}$. This is a useful relation if we know F and V and want to find H. However, suppose we know only F and the angle A at which F is inclined to the horizontal. In that case we should know a little about elementary trigonometry, but the process can be explained simply in any event. Consider the identity, $H = H$. Now multiply H by F/F to give $H = FH/F$, which is still an equality since $F/F = 1$.

Now refer to Fig. 3.1. The ratio H over F is called the cosine of the angle A and has a specific value depending only on the value of the angle. Thus, if we want to find the cosine of 30°, we can find it in trigonometry tables, or we can construct a right triangle with a 30° angle (using a protractor), measure F and H and thus find that the cosine of 30° = 0.866

The above can be demonstrated directly using algebra, since a 30° right triangle is just half of an equilateral triangle and, thus, $V = F/2$, and

$$F^2 = V^2 + H^2 = \frac{F^2}{4} + H^2 = \frac{4H^2}{3}$$

Thus

$$H = \frac{E}{2}\sqrt{3} = 0.866F$$

The cosine of 45° can also be found easily, since $V = H$. Thus cos 45° = 0.707. Also, it can easily be shown that cos 60° = 0.50.

If the child pulls his wagon by exerting a force of ten pounds at an angle of 60° to the horizontal, the effective horizontal force is only five pounds. The work done in pulling the wagon ten feet is 50 foot-pounds.

The concept of energy is closely related to that of work, and the units are identical. Energy is defined as capacity to do work, and a system is said to contain energy if it can perform useful work. Energy comes in many forms depending on what type of force is the agent doing the work. Thus there is nuclear energy (derived from the nuclear binding force), electrical energy, magnetic energy and gravitational energy derived from the four fundamental field forces. There is also the energy an object possesses because of its motion—this is *inertial* energy derived from inertial force. We should probably speak of five fundamental forces rather than four, although inertial force is not of the same character as the other four. It is not ordinarily considered a field force like gravity, electricity, etc., and yet it is also not a reaction force. Perhaps the efforts of modern physicists toward improving our understanding of these fundamental forces will soon lead to a better explanation of inertial force and possibly even the discovery of an inertial field.

The energy of motion is called *kinetic energy*. It can be derived from Newton's second law of motion in the following way:

$$F = ma$$

thus

$$Fs = mas$$

where s = distance. But Fs equals work or energy and, thus, mas also equals work or energy.

If an object with mass m is accelerated at a rate a through a distance s by the action of a force F, it will acquire the velocity v. The energy required to give the object this velocity is F times s. We learn from physics that velocity, acceleration and distance are related by the equation

$$v^2 = 2as$$

thus

$$as = \frac{v^2}{2} \quad \text{and} \quad Fs = \frac{mv^2}{2}$$

The kinetic energy of an object is its capacity for doing work because of its mass and velocity and can be found from the equation

$$KE = \frac{mv^2}{2}$$

Of equal importance in mechanics along with kinetic energy, is *potential energy*. This is the energy an object has because of its *mass* and its *position* in a force field. In astronomy and astronautics, one of the most important concepts to understand is that of gravitational potential energy.

The potential energy of an object can be found by calculating the amount of work necessary to carry the object to its present position in the force field or the work it can do because of its position.

Potential energy is always measured relative to some arbitrary, chosen, zero position such as the surface of the earth. Thus, if a mass of one slug is raised to a height of 100 feet above sea level, we can find its potential energy relative to sea level by finding the work necessary to raise it 100 feet. Thus,

$$PE = Fs = mgs$$

because $F = mg$, where g is the acceleration of gravity at sea level. Actually g will vary with altitude, but the variation in 100 feet is small and could be ignored in most cases. For the example chosen,

$$PE = 1 \times 32.2 \times 100 = 3220 \text{ foot-pounds}$$

One of the most important laws in astronomy and astronautics is that of the conservation of mechanical energy. In simple terms it states that *the total mechanical energy of an object cannot change in an environment where there is no friction.* An environment such as interplanetary space, where there is no atmosphere to cause friction losses, is called a *conservative* system.

Suppose that an object with a mass of one slug is given sufficient initial vertical velocity that it will rise 100 feet. As the object rises, its initial kinetic energy will gradually change to potential energy until, finally, at the peak of its trajectory, it will have a potential energy equal to the original kinetic energy. As the object falls back down, its potential energy is converted back to kinetic energy. When it strikes the ground, its potential energy will be zero and its kinetic energy will be equal to its initial value—if friction losses are ignored.

At any point on the trajectory the sum of the object's potential energy and kinetic energy will always be equal to the initial kinetic energy.

MOMENTUM AND IMPULSE

Returning to Newton's second law of motion, it should be noted that $F = ma$ was not its original form. Newton expressed it as $F = mv/t$, where t is time, and called the product mv the "quantity of motion." Of course, if it is assumed that the mass is constant, then

$$F = m\frac{v}{t} = ma$$

However, there are some cases where the mass is not constant, the best example being the rocket. In this case, the velocity of the exhaust gases may be constant, but the mass of the exhaust is changing. It is found that the thrust of a rocket engine, T, is equal to the exhaust velocity, c, times what is called the *mass flow rate*. Thus,

$$T = \frac{mc}{t}$$

which will be discussed further in the chapter on propulsion.

The product mv which Newton called "quantity of motion" is now called *momentum*. Like force and velocity, it is a vector quantity; that is, it has both magnitude and direction. In contrast, mass, work and energy have no direction associated with them. Such quantities are called *scalars*.

A corollary to Newton's second law is the important and fundamental *law of conservation of momentum*. If the second law is written $F = mv/t$ and the force is set equal to zero, it follows that the change in momentum is also zero. In other words, the momentum of an object will be constant unless it is acted upon by an external force. When stated as follows, *An object will continue in its state of rest or motion unless acted on by an external force,* this important corollary of the second law is also called Newton's first law of motion.

There are many important consequences of this fundamental law and it enables physicists and astronomers to solve numerous problems which would otherwise be beyond their capabilities. Consider, for example, the case of a bullet fired from a gun. Since no outside force is acting on the system, gun + bullet, their total momentum must be the same after the firing as before, that is, zero. Thus,

$$MV + mv = 0 \quad \text{or} \quad MV = -mv$$

where the large letters refer to the gun and the small to the bullet. The gun, which kicks backward as the bullet is fired forward, has a relatively large mass and relatively low "kick" velocity. The bullet, however, has a relatively low mass but high velocity. The momentum of the gun is equal in magnitude but opposite in direction to that of the bullet.

Suppose that a gun has a mass of ten pounds and a kick velocity of ten feet per second. If the bullet has a mass of 0.1 pound, the muzzle velocity is 1000 feet per second. Which of the objects has the larger kinetic energy? Since the velocity term is squared in calculating energy, it is found that most of the kinetic energy of the system is that of the bullet. Note that the masses were expressed in pounds. Either energy should be expressed in foot-poundals or the mass should first be converted into slugs. The energy would then be in foot-pounds.

In calculating the example above, it is found that the bullet carries 100 times the kinetic energy of the gun, which is the main reason why the bullet does so much more damage than the gun, even though both possess the same momentum.

Another case of more general interest is that of collision between elastic objects. If the objects are assumed to be perfectly elastic, they rebound with no loss of energy and, thus, energy as well as momentum is conserved.

The simple example of objects like steel ball bearings or billiard balls colliding is of great general interest, since the kinetic theory of gases is derived directly from this fundamental process. The molecules of gases are assumed to be perfectly elastic just like the billiard balls (actually, of course, neither are 100% elastic).

If a billiard ball of mass m and velocity v strikes a stationary ball of equal mass, what is the resulting condition of both balls? On first consideration, it would seem that there would be several possibilities of which the most likely might be that both would move forward together at half the original velocity of the first ball. This would satisfy the law of conservation of momentum. But what about energy? We can quickly prove that this would involve a loss of energy since $mv^2/2$ is twice as big as $2m(v/2)^2/2$. Also, the relative velocity between the balls must be the same after the impact as before, which would not be the case if the balls moved forward together.

Analysis will show that the correct result is that the second ball moves forward at the original velocity of the first ball and that the first ball comes to rest in the original position of the second. This is the only way in which both energy and momentum can be conserved. The problem can be solved by equating original momentum to final momentum and original energy to final energy.

A great simplification can be made in the solution of such elastic collision problems if we emphasize a principle which unfortunately is not even mentioned in some physics texts. We might call this the principle of *temporal symmetry* and state it as follows: *In an elastic collision between two objects the separation velocity must be equal in magnitude to the impact velocity.* This principle can be perceived intuitively by assuming that the two balls are colliding in free space where only their relative velocity can be detected and measured. The assumption of perfect elasticity, then, implies directly that there will be no difference betwen impact and recovery velocities—except in direction. The principle can also be derived from the laws of conservation of momentum and energy. Stated in symbols it is

$$V_1 = v_2 - V_2$$

where V_1 = initial velocity of first ball
V_2 = final velocity of first ball
v_1 = initial velocity of second ball = 0
(coordinate system can always be chosen such that this is true)
v_2 = final velocity of second ball

If V and the masses M and m are known, the final velocities can be found from the law of conservation of momentum and the principle of temporal symmetry without the use of the energy law.

$$MV_1 = MV_2 + mv_2$$

Now let $M = am$; then

$$amV_1 = amV_2 + mv_2$$

and

$$aV_1 = aV_2 + v_2$$

But we also know that

$$V_1 = v_2 - V_2$$

Thus,

$$av_2 - aV_2 = aV_2 + v_2$$

and

$$(a-1)v_2 = 2aV_2 \quad \text{or} \quad v_2 = \frac{2a}{a-1} V_2$$

Then

$$V_1 = V_2 + \frac{2V_2}{a-1} = \frac{a+1}{a-1} V_2$$

or

$$V_2 = \frac{a-1}{a+1} V_1$$

and

$$v_2 = V_2 + V_1 = \left(\frac{a-1}{a+1} + 1\right) V_1 = \frac{2a}{a+1} V_1$$

Thus the final velocity of the second ball, v_2, is equal to

$$\frac{2M}{M+m}$$

times the initial velocity of the first ball, V_1. If $M = m$, then $v_2 = V_1$.

This is much simpler than the usual process involving the kinetic energy since the energy terms contain the velocity squared.

The principle of temporal symmetry is not just a different statement of the law of conservation of energy since it is independent of mass and is only of the first order in velocity (that is, it does not contain any velocity-squared terms). It states simply that *an elastic collision is symmetrical in time about the impact point.*

Of particular importance in the field of rocket propulsion is a quantity which can be equated to momentum called *impulse.*

If the relation $F = mv/t$ is multiplied by t, it becomes, $Ft = mv$. The right side is what is called momentum; the left side is called *impulse.*

If a rocket engine exerts a thrust T for a time t, the product Tt is called the impulse. If the entire propellant supply of the rocket is consumed during the burning time t, then Tt is called the *total impulse.*

Note that the units of momentum in the English Gravitational System are foot-slugs per second and the units of impulse are pound-seconds. In the MKS system the corresponding units would be kilogram-meters per second and Newton seconds.

CHAPTER 4

The Earth

"A SMEAR OF biology on a speck of cosmic dust" is the way the renowned astronomer Harlow Shapley once described life on our earth. In truth, cosmically speaking, we do live on a speck of dust but this speck is some 8000 miles in diameter and represents our home in space. This home moves with many motions, but because the motion is so smooth and so effortless the earth seems to be a stable platform around which swirl the sun, moon, planets and stars. In reality, the motion of the earth is so complex that some scientists have made and are making a career of just interpreting these motions. Some of the motions are quite easily discernible whereas others can only be surmised from the behavior of the heavens. In the fourth century B.C., Heracleides of Pontus correctly interpreted the rotation of the earth. The philosophers at that time realized that the stars were so distant that to visualize the earth stationary with the heavens rotating around the earth was completely unrealistic. Thus from earliest times, imaginative philosophers have interpreted the apparent motions of the sun, moon, planets and stars around the earth as due to the diurnal motion of the earth.

MOTIONS OF THE EARTH

However, this motion is but one of many recognized today. Astronomers know the earth circles the sun once in the 365¼ days of a year. This is the annual motion of the earth in its orbit around the sun. But to be realistic about this motion, we must consider the moon. The earth-moon system may be considered a twin planet. It is this twin planet that orbits the sun in a smooth ellipse. There is a center of gravity of this twin system, the *barycenter,* and it is this barycenter which moves in the smooth ellipse we picture as the orbit of the earth. Actually, the barycenter is contained within the earth, for it is 3000 miles from the center in the direction of the moon. In other words, it is 1000 miles beneath the surface of the earth on a line joining the centers of the earth and moon. Thus, while the barycenter moves in an elliptical path, the earth is moving in a wave-like pattern around the barycenter path. Thus 12⅓ times during the course of the year the center of the earth oscillates about this curve.

From measures made of the sky, astronomers find that the sun is moving in the general direction of the constellation Hercules with a speed of about 12 miles per second. As the earth is a member of the solar system, it must also be moving in this direction, and the motion of the earth can be pictured as a sort of helix.

As a member of the Milky Way galaxy, the sun is constrained to move around the center of this system with a speed of about 175 miles per second. At the sun's distance from the center of the galaxy, it means that even with this speed the sun, and with it the earth, will take about 200,000,000 years to make a single circuit of the center.

These, then, are some of the motions of which our "stable" earth partakes.

STRUCTURE OF THE EARTH

The motion of the earth has influenced the shape of the earth, which is not a perfect sphere. The Greek philosopher Pythagoras, in the sixth century B.C., correctly speculated on the shape of the earth. Because the sphere was considered to be the perfect figure, it was thought that the earth must also partake of this shape. Later the Greeks, by observing the shadow of the earth on the moon, concluded that since only a spherical body could always cast round shadows, the earth must indeed be a sphere. Thus, in early days it was known that the earth rotates and is a sphere.

Actually, the centrifugal force, resulting from the rotation of the earth, forces the earth to assume the shape of an oblate spheroid. An oblate spheroid is a slightly squashed sphere like a grapefruit or an orange. The diameter through the equator of the earth exceeds the diameter through the poles by 26.7 miles. This corresponds to a flattening or oblateness of 1/297.

The question of oblateness and shape of the earth is also intimately linked to the structure of the earth. Through the science of seismology, the study of earth vibrations, scientists have un-

Fig. 4-1   Section of earth showing layers and solid core.

Illus.: The Decker Corp.

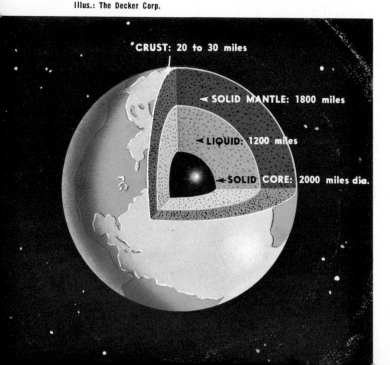

CRUST: 20 to 30 miles

◄ SOLID MANTLE: 1800 miles

◄ LIQUID: 1200 miles

◄ SOLID CORE: 2000 miles dia.

covered clues to the structure of the earth. Although we believe we know approximately this structure, research now underway may radically alter this picture. Today scientists are boring a hole in the bottom of the sea to break through the crust of the earth to bring up samples of the mantle material. The results from these test borings may have a profound influence on our picture of the structure of the earth. If these borings succeed in their mission, the impact on the earth sciences may inaugurate a new scientific era.

Today science has uncovered several distinct layers of the earth (see Figure 4-1). The topmost layer, the one on which we live, is the crust. In thickness it varies from three to five miles on the floor of the ocean to somewhat more than 20 miles for the land masses. This crust is uniform neither in thickness nor in composition. Because the mass of the crust turns out to be uniform, we discover that the dense materials beneath the seas give rise to a thinner layer over the mantle. Where there are mountains with less dense materials, the crust will go down deeper into the mantle and actual "mountain roots" will depress the mantle.

The continental land masses are certainly less dense than the underlying mantle material, which makes them behave like large ice masses floating in water. The laws of equilibrium come into play so that if we were to section the top, say, 20 miles of the earth's surface, the mass of these sections, no matter where on earth they were made, would be the same. Scientists have created the term *isostasy* for this condition and hold that natural forces in the earth always have as their goal isostatic equilibrium.

Beneath the crust we find the Mohorovicic discontinuity, named for the Croatian seismologist, Andrja Mohorovicic, who discovered this break in 1909. This is a well-defined boundary separating the crust from the mantle at which seismic waves abruptly increase in velocity. The mantle extends down to a depth of about 1800 miles. Below the mantle is presumed to exist a liquid core over 1000 miles thick and, finally, there is the solid core of the earth which is somewhat less than 2000 miles in diameter.

Not too long ago, it was believed that the center of the earth was liquid because some of the seismic waves could not pass through this center. Today a new picture has evolved. The fact that the S (shear) or secondary waves do not travel through the center of the earth means that a liquid shell surrounds the core. The P or primary waves which consist of condensations and rarefactions like sound waves can travel through a liquid. But the S waves which travel from side to side, like a snake, cannot be transmitted through a liquid. Thus, the failure to record them at some points on the earth's surface after an earthquake indicates the fluidity of some portions of the inner earth. From a careful study of the shadow belts where the S waves do not arrive at the surface, it has become possible to trace the size of this liquid shell.

At the center of the earth there is a solid core of high density and under considerable pressure. At the bottom of the ocean the pressure is defined by the weight of water which lies over it; thus, the pressure can be greater than 10,000 pounds per square inch. At the center of the earth the pressure, which again can be defined as the weight of overlying material, increases to 60,000,000 pounds per square inch!

The mass of the earth is a significant feature in its role as our home. The force of gravity, the velocity of escape and the motions of the earth-moon system are all intimately related to the amount of material in the earth. The question raised a long time ago was, "How do we, who live on the surface of the earth, find the mass or amount of material in it?"

Almost 200 years ago the English astronomer, Nevil Maskelyne, suspended a pendulum near the large mountain Schiehallien in Perthshire and discovered that it did not hang vertically. The shift in its position he attributed to the mass of the nearby mountain. What happened was that the earth attracted the pendulum and tried to make it hang vertically. At the same time the mountain attracted the pendulum and made it move to one side. Thus, the deflection was a function of the mass of the mountain. The more massive the mountain, the greater the deflection. This meant that if the mass of the mountain could be determined, the mass of the earth could be determined. As the mountain was a regular one without odd shapes it was possible to compute the size and, with some assumptions, the mass of the mountain and from that the mass of the earth.

Shortly thereafter, in 1797–8, the distinguished English scientist, Henry Cavendish, performed a laboratory experiment of extreme delicacy in which he determined the mass of the earth by the deflection of two small balls attracted to two large lead balls. The results of the experiments indicated that the mass of the earth is 5.98×10^{27} grams or 6.78×10^{21} tons or 6780 million million million tons.

Knowing the size of the earth and its mass, it is possible to determine the average density of the earth. The computation discloses that the average density of the earth is 5.5 times that of water. We know that the density of rocks, both surface and those below the surface thrown out by volcanoes, are at the very most 3.3. This means that the central density must be greater than 5.5 to average out the low surface density. The density in the mantle is five times that of water. At the liquid core it is 11 times that of water and, finally, the solid core must be 14 times as dense as

Fig. 4-2 **The earth's magnetic field.**

Illus.: The Decker Corp.

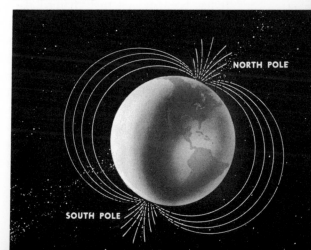

water. Thus the material in the center of the earth is denser than mercury.

The earth is a huge magnet of mysterious origin which has influenced the affairs of man from earliest times. To account for this magnetic field scientists suggest that it may be created by a dynamo-like action in the earth's nickel-iron core. The magnetic field of the earth has provided a reference for navigators from which they could determine position on the earth's surface. In the affairs of man, this feature has proven one of the most significant concerning the earth. In comparatively recent times, the presence of a magnetic field has unraveled some of the mystery surrounding the arrival of particles from space and the behavior of phenomena in the upper atmosphere.

RADIATION BELTS

In April 1956, Professor S. Fred Singer, of the University of Maryland, postulated that the presence of a terrestrial magnetic field would trap charged particles coming from space and constrain them to move in paths which would also concentrate them. He postulated the existence of at least two doughnut-shaped belts containing charged particles. In 1958, information telemetered back to the earth by Explorer I permitted Professor James van Allen and his colleagues to prove that indeed there were radiation belts in the sky, with the nearer one most intense and the distant one larger but possessing a lower level of radiation.

It has been proved that charged particles moving toward the earth are trapped by the magnetic field of the earth. The particles spiral down the magnetic lines and, as they approach the earth at the northern or southern end of the radiation belt, the spirals become tighter and tighter. Finally, they are reflected back and the particles begin to spiral in the other direction. Thus the particles oscillate back and forth between the two hemispheres of the earth.

Since the initial discovery of the two radiation belts, information from the 83-pound Explorer XII launched on August 15, 1961 has developed a new concept of the earth's immediate environment. This satellite moved in a highly eccentric orbit with a 26.5

Fig. 4-3 Section through principal radiation belts around earth.

Illus.: General Features Corp.

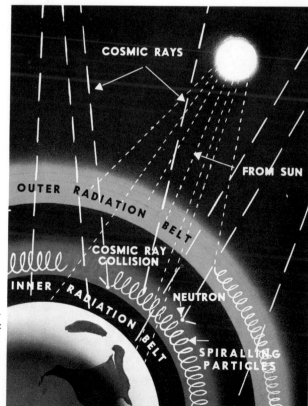

COSMIC RAYS

FROM SUN

OUTER RADIATION BELT

COSMIC RAY COLLISION

INNER RADIATION BELT

NEUTRON

SPIRALLING PARTICLES

Fig. 4-4 Trapping of particles by magnetic field of the earth.

Illus.: The Decker Corp.

hour period. At perigee it came within 182 miles of the earth's surface, whereas at apogee it moved out to 48,000 miles. Thus it could explore space beyond the reach of previous satellites. The new picture resulting from its data reveals a totally different concept of the earth's radiation belts.

Results from the 12-day active life of Explorer XII indicate that the earth is circled by a pulsing toroid of trapped charged particles of various energies in many belts. Scientists have named this region the *magnetosphere* because it is here that particles are trapped by the geomagnetic field. It could be thought of as a tremendous single belt over 45,000 miles deep which contains concentrations of particles of particular energies in well-defined zones. The inner edge of the magnetosphere is rather sharp, whereas the outer boundary "breathes" in and out. Where the outer boundary ends depends on the activity of the sun and the particles, or solar wind, coming in toward the earth from the sun. Beyond the outer edge of the magnetosphere there exists a turbulent region some 12,000 miles deep with fluctuating magnetic fields and solar winds. Beyond this point, interplanetary space begins. As the magnetosphere tapers off at the poles, there exists a region over the earth's magnetic poles which is relatively free of radiation and, therefore, of extreme interest to those who will venture into space.

The radiation belts are not the only layers above the earth's surface which are electrified in nature. To speak about these layers it is necessary to discuss the earth's atmosphere in detail.

ATMOSPHERE

Our presence on the surface of the earth means we live beneath a thick, turbulent atmosphere which extends up 1000 miles. The bottom layer of this atmosphere, the one in which we live, is called the *troposphere*. It is not uniform in thickness but increases as we go to the equator until it becomes 12 miles thick. It is in this layer that weather is made. Since 75% of the mass of the atmosphere lies in this layer, its composition is in reality the composition of the atmosphere. Nitrogen makes up 78% of the atmosphere and life-giving oxygen comprises another 21%. All of the other gases in the atmosphere comprise but one per cent. These include carbon dioxide, water vapor, hydrogen, helium and traces of the other rare gases.

At sea level, about 400 million million million molecules of air are found in each cubic inch. They are so closely packed that each particle often collides with another. We call the average distance between collisions the *mean free path,* and at sea level it is about one-millionth of an inch.

The temperature in this bottom layer varies with altitude. At the surface the temperature is about 60 degrees and, as we ascend, the temperature drops until finally, at the top of the layer, the temperature approaches 85 degrees Fahrenheit below zero.

Above the troposphere lies the *stratosphere* and the boundary between these layers is called the *tropopause.* Curiously, this thin boundary is slightly warmer than the troposphere. The stratosphere extends about 20 miles above the earth's surface. In this layer the air has become quite tenuous and the temperature declines from 40 degrees Fahrenheit below zero to 85 degrees Fahrenheit below zero at a height of about 12 miles; then it curiously rises to about 35 degrees Fahrenheit below zero at the stratopause, the top of this layer. So thin is the air here that clouds and storms generally do not develop. However, the thread-like cirrus clouds, composed of ice crystals, are in the stratosphere, as are also the strange, mysterious "mother-of-pearl" clouds whose origin and composition are unknown.

Above the stratopause, at an altitude of 20 miles, lies the *chemosphere* which extends to a height of 50 miles. At the stratopause the temperature is 35 degrees below zero Fahrenheit. By the time we have reached an altitude of 30 miles, the temperature has risen to 30 degrees Fahrenheit. From this point to the top of the chemosphere, the temperature steadily declines to 90 degrees below zero Fahrenheit.

The 30-mile layer comprising the chemosphere is, in reality, an enormous photochemical laboratory. There the ultraviolet radiations from the sun produce strange chemical reactions. Ultraviolet

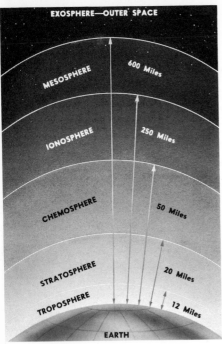

Fig. 4-5 Structure of the atmosphere.

Illus.: The Decker Corp.

radiation breaks up the oxygen molecule into atomic oxygen which then combines with the oxygen molecule to form ozone. Other radiations break up the ozone molecule into molecular and atomic oxygen, preventing the ozone layer from becoming too thick. Without ozone in our atmosphere, too much ultraviolet radiation would filter through to the surface of the earth and life would be strangely different, if not quite impossible. Because ozone possesses the peculiar property of absorbing heat from solar radiation, it accounts for the increase in temperature in the high stratosphere and low chemosphere.

IONOSPHERE

Above the chemosphere and extending for about 200 miles is the *ionosphere*. Although there are distinct layers to the ionosphere, we might think of the entire 200-mile region as composed of ionized or fractured atoms. These particles are the remains of atoms which have been broken up or disrupted by the intense shortwave solar radiations. Thus the ionosphere is most sensitive to the arrival of high-energy radiations from the sun which possess this disrupting ability. At the time of a solar flare, when a flood of ultraviolet radiation, X-rays and gamma rays come into the atmosphere of the earth and increase the shortwave radiations by 100,000 fold, the layers expand and the charged particles become more concentrated in the layers.

In addition to the layers of ions, this region is also the one in which meteors burn out and the region where glows in the sky originate. The most important of these glows are the auroral displays—the northern and southern lights. Aurorae can be found extending much higher than the top of the chemosphere, but very rarely do they descend lower.

Recently there has been a rediscussion on the cause of these lights. Dr. James van Allen and his colleagues at the State University of Iowa launched an "Injun" satellite to determine their cause. This satellite possessed multiple proton counters pointed across and along the earth's magnetic lines of force. In this way, these scientists hope to disclose whether the aurorae are caused by particles from the radiation belts or by particles coming directly from the sun. It is believed that the radiation belts are somewhat elastic, and when they become too full, the particles are dumped out of the ends, resulting in an influx of protons which in turn excite the atmospheric molecules to give rise to the auroral lights.

The temperature in the ionosphere rises continuously from 90 degrees below zero to about 350 degrees above zero at a height of 120 miles. By the time one reaches the ionopause the temperature is in excess of several hundred degrees. By the time the top of the atmosphere is reached the temperature has risen to several thousand degrees.

One must be most careful not to interpret this temperature in terms of heat. Temperature is simply a measure of how fast particles travel. At the surface of the earth the molecules of air are so closely packed that they can not achieve high speeds. However, the mean free path at a height of 70 miles is about 51 inches; at 140 miles it is about 3600 feet; at 250 miles, the top of the ionosphere, particles travel 43 miles before they collide with one another. They travel fast, but because there are so few of them they can produce no sensation of heat as we understand it.

In the ionosphere there are layers of electrons that provide re-flecting layers for radio waves. Without these layers, it would be impossible to receive radio signals beyond the horizon. We owe these layers to the sun's ultraviolet radiation which tears electrons from the air molecules. In terms of electron content, the lowest layers possess the least number of electrons.

The D layer, the lowest one, is probably actually in the chemosphere, or at best very low in the ionosphere. It reflects long waves with frequencies of from ten to 500 kilocycles per second but permits the shorter radio waves to pass through un-hindered. The E layer, with about 1,500,000 electrons per cubic inch lies at an average height of about 75 miles and reflects the familiar radio broadcast bands. The F_1 layer, with about 3,000,000 electrons per cubic inch, averages 120 miles in altitude and reflects regular shortwave signals. The F_2 layer is more than 150 miles high and reflects still shorter waves. This layer has about 15,000,-000 electrons per cubic inch and probably here the electron concentration is a maximum. Scientists believe there is still another uncertain electron stratum, the G layer, which lies above the ionosphere. Television and FM radio waves, much shorter still, are normally not reflected by any of these layers but pass through uninterrupted.

Fig. 4-6

Illus.: The Decker Corp.

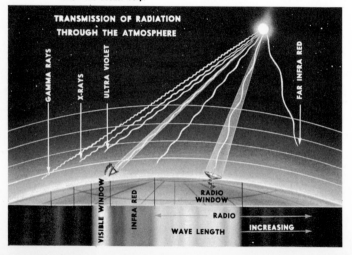

Changes occur in the layers, both in height and in electron density, and their characteristics are under intense investigation almost constantly. We know they are formed by solar ultraviolet and X-ray waves because the time of day, the season of the year, the latitude of the observer and the condition of the sun's activity all produce changes. Sometimes, inexplicably, there appear to be denser clouds of electrons concentrated in these layers so that even TV and FM signals will be reflected and programs may be picked up from great distances.

In 1962 scientists studying the structure of the atmosphere discovered evidence that it was layered very much like a cake. From the surface to about 55 miles was called the *homosphere* which consisted of the primary components of the atmosphere, nitrogen, oxygen and argon, uniformly mixed in their standard proportions. Above the homosphere and stretching for about 22,000 miles was the *heterosphere*. At an altitude of 22,000 miles the particles move synchronously with the earth and, thus, maintain their positions over a given area of the earth.

From 55 miles, the base of the heterosphere, and rising to 125 miles is the layer of nitrogen. Above this to a height of 700 miles we find a layer of oxygen. Helium next forms a shell around the earth out to a distance of 2200 miles. From 2200 miles to 22,000 miles is the *protonosphere* composed of hydrogen.

Above 250 miles so few particles exist that there are too few electrons to form reflecting layers for radio waves. However, auroral displays are formed in this layer and can extend downward into lower regions. Only a few billion molecules per cubic inch are necessary, however, for such displays.

Beyond 600 miles the particle density becomes so low that collisions seldom occur. Thus, at this region, particles of the earth's atmosphere can escape into space. Here, perhaps, is what can be called the "top" of the atmosphere. So few particles are present that their effects on objects passing through this region are minimal. Only when its effects on large, low-mass satellites in this region are studied do we become conscious of its presence.

CHAPTER 5

The Moon

BEFORE THE END of the 1960's man will be on the moon. Putting man on the moon means that for the first time he will possess a stable platform away from the earth from which he can observe the skies and, what may be even more important, a suitable takeoff place from which to explore the remainder of the solar system and, if he so desires, reach out for the stars.

The brightest object in the night sky is the moon. For thousands of years men have dreamed of some day setting foot on it. Man's imagery in visiting the moon is embodied in writings which date from the beginning of the Christian era. However, lunar visits are only now approaching the realm of possibility, with science and technology at the advanced stage necessary to make the trip possible. This event will satisfy a mysterious desire of the human race to walk on the lunar surface.

To understand the role the moon will play in the exploration of space, it is first necessary to understand its physical characteristics. Let's explore the moon and familiarize ourselves with these features.

The origin of the moon is shrouded in mystery. We have no definitive proof as to when or how it came into being. During the last century it was popular to assume that the moon was once part of the earth and was torn out of the Pacific basin during the early history of the earth. Sir George H. Darwin, in 1878, suggested that in the distant past the moon had been part of the earth, and, at that time, the day was four hours in length. The earth rotated with this period creating two tides daily due to the tidal action of the sun. Since the natural period of the earth is also four hours, a resonance could have occurred which could have increased the amplitude of the tides. Finally, the earth became unstable and, to regain its equilibrium, threw off a large segment of one tidal bulge; thus the moon was born. The Pacific basin is pointed out to be the scar on the earth left when the moon was separated.

Sir Harold Jeffreys, in a study of this problem about 30 years ago, showed that so much energy would have to be dissipated to viscous friction under these conditions that the tides could never become large enough to cause one of the bulges to be thrown off to form the moon.

Today most scientists believe that the earth-moon system was formed four to five billion years ago as a twin planet. Whatever theory is invoked for the creation of the earth and moon, it is generally assumed they had a common parent and the same material found on the earth should also be found on the moon.

Like the earth, the moon is a "dark body" and has no light of its

Fig. 5-1 The Moon—Ages 3 days and 5 days.

Illus.: Mt. Wilson and Mt. Palomar Observatories

own. The only reason we see the moon is that the sun shines on it, enabling us to see it by reflected sunlight. The moon also revolves around the earth. Thus it appears in different positions with respect to the earth. When the moon is directly in line with the sun, the sunlit half is turned away from us. This is the new moon, and we do not see it unless it comes directly in front of the sun as at the time of a solar eclipse. After one day the new moon, in its motion around the earth, can be seen as a thin crescent. With the passage of more time the moon moves farther around the earth until it reaches a point in its orbit where the earth lies between it and the sun. At that time we can see the entire moon illuminated —this is the full moon. The phases then reverse themselves until the moon once more is new.

The moon spins on its axis. Once in the 27⅓ days of the *sidereal* month the moon completes a rotation. If you were on the moon and observed a star due south, the time it would take the moon to rotate until that star came back to the meridian is the sidereal month of 27⅓ days. With respect to the sun, it takes the moon somewhat longer to return. While the moon is turning around the earth, the earth is also moving around the sun. Thus, if we see the moon at a particular phase, say the full moon, the time it takes to go from full moon to full moon is 29½ days. This is the *synodic* month.

Fig. 5-2 **The moon at first quarter.**
Illus.: Lick Observatory

Fig. 5-3 **The moon at third quo**
Illus.: Lick Obser

Astronomers who have studied the motion of the moon know that the moon does not move as uniformly as might be suspected. For example, the sidereal month indicated above is an average length. Because of the perturbations, the length of the sidereal month may vary by as much as seven hours. By the same token, because of the eccentricity of the moon's orbit and the resulting non-uniform motion of the moon, the synodic month may vary by as much as 13 hours. Thus the lengths of the months usually given in text books are average values, and only rarely are they achieved exactly during one lunation.

The subject of the motions of the moon is called *lunar theory*. It represents one of the most difficult and abstruse facets of astronomy. Although the motions are most difficult to study, we can describe some of the principal ones. The inordinate variety of motions is due to the fact that the earth and moon are not the only two bodies in space. Because there is a sun and planets, it means that each of these bodies through their mass will disturb the moon. These perturbations must be recognized in trying to describe the moon's motion precisely.

There is a motion called the *Variation* which is the difference between the true moon position and the position the moon would occupy if it moved around the earth in a circle. As the moon moves

Fig. 5-4 Two photographs showing the moon of the same age. The differences in appearance are due to librations.

Illus.: Lick Observatory

from new to first quarter, it may be as much as 2500 miles ahead of the place it would occupy if the moon moved in a circle. Between third quarter and new the moon may be 2500 miles behind the position in the circular orbit. The effect is to make the new and full moons occur too early, whereas the moon at the quarter is somewhat late in the cycle.

Although we could talk about effects like the *Variation,* the *Evection, Regression* of the *Nodes,* the *Annual Equation,* etc., these are technical terms which do not concern anyone except research astronomers. Lunar experts can break the motions of the moon down into 300 principal, periodic motions. Half of these are along the ecliptic, the other half perpendicular to it. For this reason we will restrict ourselves to discussing motions which have significance to us.

The moon undergoes *librations* or slight oscillating motions permitting us to see beyond the edge of the moon. The moon's equator is tipped about 6½° to the plane of the ecliptic, the earth's orbit around the sun. Thus, as the moon swings around the earth, we can at one time of the month peer over the north pole and a half-month later we can peer over the south pole, for the poles are alternately tipped toward and away from us. This results in a latitudinal libration.

The moon rotates on its axis uniformly, but in its motion around the earth it is moving in an ellipse and thus when it is close to the earth (perigee) it is moving faster than a half-month later when it is at apogee. This longitudinal libration permits us to peer around the east and west limbs of the moon by about 8°.

There is another libration which is usually recognized. The diurnal libration is due to the rotation of the earth. As the earth rotates an observer on the earth will see the moon from slightly different angles. Thus, when the moon is rising or setting, he can see about 1° over the upper limb of the moon. The net result of these librations of the moon permits an observer on the earth to see 59% of the lunar surface. Actually, we alternately see 18% and always see 41%. Thus 41% of the moon is never seen. This is the side of the moon turned away from us.

There is a good reason why the moon always keeps the same side toward the earth. Astronomers believe that a long time ago—some four or five billion years ago—the moon was much closer to the earth and at that time may still have been in a plastic state. With the moon so close, the tidal action of the earth on the moon pulled out a tide on the moon in the direction of the earth. Thus the moon became shaped like a modified football with the "long" axis pointed toward the earth. The excess of the long axis is only 3600 feet over the other two. As time went on the moon congealed. Now the gravitational pull of the earth came into play to capture the long axis and constrain the moon always to keep the long axis pointed toward the earth. Thus we never see the other side of the moon.

The size of the moon and its distance from the earth have been known for a long time. Aristarchus, during the third century B.C., not only found a rough answer to the size and distance of the moon in terms of the diameter of the earth, but he also proved the sun was larger than the earth. This was an amazing discovery, for without instruments this resulted purely from inductive reasoning.

The critical observation made by Aristarchus was the time of the quarter moon. He constructed a triangle with the earth, moon, sun system. At the time of quarter moon these are positioned to form a right triangle. The angle at the earth Aristarchus assumed to be 87°. Thus the angle between the lines drawn from the sun to the moon and from the sun to the earth was but 3°. From this he concluded that the earth-sun distance was about 19 times the earth-moon distance. Today we know this is incorrect. The sun is roughly 400 times as distant as the moon.

Today the moon's distance can be determined rather readily with the aid of telescopes. The moon can be seen by observers from widely scattered points on the earth's surface. These observers can pick a particular crater or peak on the moon and, knowing the distance between the stations on the earth, they can derive the distance to the moon. The mean distance from the earth to the moon is 238,857 miles. Because of the eccentricity and perturbations of the moon's orbit, it can come as close as 221,463 miles and it can recede to 252,710 miles.

Knowing the distance to the moon makes it possible to measure its diameter—2160 miles. This finding permits a determination of the volume of the moon. Now, if we could determine the mass of the moon, we could find the density. It is possible to determine the mass. The method which astronomers use is to find the motion of the two bodies around their common center of gravity. By finding the earth distance and the moon distance from the barycenter, a ratio of masses can be determined. It is found that the moon has a mass 1/81.5 times that of the earth. With this mass the density of the moon is 3.31.

The gravitational pull of a celestial body is determined both by its size and mass. Since the moon is one-fourth the size of the earth and has so much less mass, we would expect that the moon's gravitational pull would also be less than the earth's. Actually, the pull of gravity on the surface of the moon is one-sixth of that on the earth. Thus a 150-pound man on the earth would weigh only 25 pounds on the moon. With the pull of gravity less and the velocity of escape tied directly to this force, it means that the velocity of escape on the moon is considerably less than on the earth. On the earth the velocity of escape is seven miles per second and on the moon it is about 1½ miles per second. Satellite velocity being $1/\sqrt{2}$ times escape velocity means that orbital velocity for the moon is one mile per second compared to about five miles per second for the earth.

It is this low escape velocity which puts such a high premium on getting to the moon. The low velocity means that the energy necessary to get a space vehicle away from the moon on trips to perhaps other members of the solar system is so much less than that necessary for the earth that some scientists believe the complete and total conquest of the moon is essential to fulfill our space aspirations.

Also, the low velocity of escape means that the moon has no atmosphere in the sense that we speak of an atmosphere on the earth. There have been many attempts to measure the atmosphere of the moon using various methods, and the results range from one-millionth to a ten-million-millionth of the atmosphere of the earth. In all probability the moon at one time did have an atmosphere, but the lower gravitational field quickly permitted the atmosphere to escape into interplanetary space.

The reason why a thin atmosphere of perhaps one-millionth that of the earth may be present is that the moon apparently possesses active gas sources which emit gases under certain conditions. In November 1958, the Russian astronomer, Professor N. A. Kozyrev discovered gas coming from the mountain peak in the moon crater Alphonsus. This crater had for a long time been suspected of being filled with some sort of obscuring material. The American astronomer Dinsmore Alter took photographs of this area in ultraviolet and infrared which showed marked obscuration in the UV pictures. These obscurations were probably due to the gases. When Kozyrev took spectograms of these gases which were excited by the shortwave radiations of the sun, he discovered that the gases, at least in part, were comprised of two- and three-atom carbon molecules.

As in the case of the earth, there may be radioactive deposits under the lunar surface which create enough heat to melt the rocks

Fig. 5-5 The white arrow marks the mountain peak in the crater alphonsus. It is from this peak that gases have been seen to escape.

Illus.: Mt. Wilson and Mt. Palomar Observatories

and cause them to give up their gases. These gases are probably trapped in caves, and when the surface is ruptured or disturbed by moonquakes, the gases can come to the surface. The presence of the gases also indicates to astronomers that the caves needed for shelter when man gets to the moon may be available, so that the hazards of space will be minimized.

The surface of the moon is an alien and unfriendly place. Without the moderating influence of an atmosphere, the radiant energy of an overhead sun raises the temperatures to high levels. Directly beneath the sun, the temperature can go above the boiling point of water. The same place some two weeks later, when the sun is below the horizon, has a temperature of 240° below zero Fahrenheit. In fact, when you are on the day side, you may feel very hot, and when you step into the shadow of a cliff or an overhanging rock, the temperature may drop precipitously. Without an atmosphere the radiations which are present in space will strike the moon with full intensity. There will be no attenuating medium to reduce the impact of the radiation.

In space there are meteoroids—tiny particles of cosmic dust which, at the moon's distance from the sun, can move with speeds up to 25 miles per second. If you add to this the speed of the moon as it moves with the earth around the sun, the closing speed of these meteoroids can go as high as 45 miles per second. Even a grain of sand moving with this speed has the energy of a high-powered rifle bullet. A piece the size of a walnut or a chestnut can do significant damage to a large structure and may create shock waves which would kill anything within the structure. Thus the surface is a most unhealthy place. These are the reasons why the first men on the moon should move underground into caves for their protection.

What we see on the moon is determined by the time we choose to look at it. At the time of the thin crescent moon there is very little to see. In a telescope we may see the sunlit crescent with little detail and the rest of the moon illuminated by earthshine, that is, sunlight reflected from the earth. Before the first quarter we begin to see clearly differentiated areas on the moon. There are dark regions which have roughly round shapes and there are bright areas which are really the rough areas on the moon. At first quarter the Caucasus and part of the Alps Mountains in the northern hemisphere are visible.

When the moon is ten days old it is seen at its very best through the telescope. The mountain ranges are visible and the dark areas are quite pronounced. The southern hemisphere is very bright and we begin to see the true nature of this area, pock-marked with a tremendous number of craters. However, when the full moon is viewed through a telescope, it is a disappointment. At this phase the sun is coming down on the moon's center from directly overhead and no shadows are cast. As a result we find the moon a relatively smooth body with only differences in shade between various sections. It is bright or dark with all sorts of gradation in between.

Look at a photograph of the full moon. The most striking features will be the division into bright and dark areas and the rays which streak across the surface. The dark areas are relatively smooth, whereas the bright areas are composed of craters, mountains, rocks, rills, valleys and other features of an incredibly rough nature—features which will remain rough because of the virtual absence of erosion.

Fig. 5-6 The full moon.

Illus.: Lick Observatory

The craters range in size from objects about 150 miles in diameter to pits barely discernible with the largest telescopes. About 30,000 craters have been counted and it is estimated that several hundred thousand others are randomly distributed over the surface.

When we speak of craters, volcanic craters come to mind. However, most lunar craters are completely unlike volcanic craters. The majority of the lunar craters resulted from unprecedented cataclysmic impacts of huge meteoroids on the surface. The typical lunar crater is a great circular ring of rock. The floor of the crater is usually lower than the area surrounding it. The inside of the crater reveals a steep wall, whereas the outer wall gently slopes into the lunar surface. From the floors of many craters rise giant mountain peaks to heights of almost 8000 feet. Yet in most cases the mountain is insignificant compared to the crater itself. As an example, Tycho, with a diameter of 54 miles, has walls which tower 15,000 feet above the deepest portion of the floor from which is thrust a peak one mile high. The rim height is about 5500 feet above the surrounding area.

Some of the largest craters are so big that even a three-mile high rim is invisible from the center. Such is the case of Clavius, 146 miles in diameter. Another provocative feature is that if the crater wall were straightened out it would create a mountain range 450

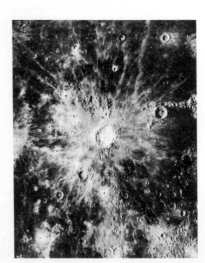

Fig. 5-7 The crater copernicus seen just before full moon. The prominent ray system is visible.

Illus.: Mt. Wilson and Mt. Palomar Observatories

miles long with a height in excess of one mile. This mountain range could completely encircle the state of New Jersey with a considerable section remaining to separate New York and Pennsylvania. And Clavius is only one of eight craters larger than 100 miles on our side of the moon.

When the early scientists turned their crude telescopes on the moon, they interpreted the dark regions as smooth places. Because they looked like bodies of water, Johannes Hevelius in 1647 called them *maria,* a Latin word meaning seas. To these they gave exotic names like Mare Serenitatis, the sea of serenity; Mare Tranquillitatis, the sea of tranquility and Mare Crisium, the sea of crises.

When astronomers discovered the moon had no water they knew the seas could not exist. They recognized the seas as comparable to the harsh deserts on the earth. But once named they could not be "unnamed." Thus the names persist.

Until recently astronomers were at a loss to explain their origin. About ten years ago Dr. Ralph B. Baldwin, building on a theory proposed by Dr. G. K. Gilbert more than 60 years ago, proposed

Fig. 5-8 The southern half of the moon at third quarter. Clavius is the largest crater on this photograph.

!llus.: Mt. Wilson and Mt. Palomar Observatories

Fig. 5-8A Northern portion of the moon at last quarter showing the region from Copernicus to the limb—100-inch telescope.

Illus.: Mt. Wilson and Mt. Palomar Observatories

that four or five billion years ago a giant chunk of rock—a *plane-tesimal*—some 125 to 200 miles in diameter struck the moon in the Mare Imbrium region with a speed of about 1½ miles per second. The precise mechanism of the resulting catastrophe is highly speculative, but astronomers generally agree that as a result of this impact an inordinate amount of energy was liberated. Whether this was all transformed into heat or whether it crushed the surface to loose a flood of lava is unknown. The significant point is that the impact triggered a mechanism which loosed this flood of lava which eventually covered half the side we see.

The resulting lava flowed to the west to form Mare Serenitatis, Mare Tranquillatis, Mare Foecunditatis and Mare Nectaris. The lava flowed to the south and east to form Mare Nubium and Oceanus Procellarum. Violent projectiles and explosions ripped along the surface through mountains to blast valleys and furrows traceable back to the impact point. Thus came into being most of the visible features of the moon.

The dark areas represent the newest features on the moon. These areas lie in the north and swing both east and west. Near the south pole are areas which were essentially in their present condition long before the impact of the giant planetesimal. These incredibly rough regions, the badlands, are considered the old moon.

The impact mechanism of the giant planetesimal has been used

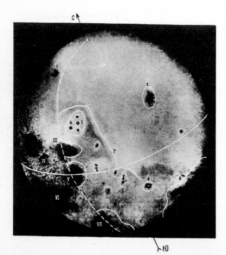

Fig. 5-9 Picture of the hidden side of the moon transmitted to the earth by Lunik III. To the left of the broken white line is that area of the moon which can be seen from the earth. To the right represents half, or about 20%, of the 41% we never see from the earth.

Illus.: Sovfoto

by one of the authors to arrive at a statistical picture of the hidden side of the moon. This picture has in many ways been substantiated by the pictures returned to the earth by Lunik III.

The reasoning in deducing such a picture goes something like this: if one carefully observes the edge of the moon during its libratory motions, it is seen that all but one of the small seas are complete. If there were a giant sea complex on the hidden side similar to the one we see, then some of the sea areas should be seen during the libratory motions. But evidence of a giant sea complex is lacking. Thus it was concluded that if a large planetesimal struck the hidden side it must have done so precisely in the center, and the odds are all against an event like this. From this reasoning it was concluded that the other side of the moon cannot be similar to our side but must in its entirety be similar to the southern region which is overrun by craters.

By counting craters on the southern hemisphere of the moon in certain size ranges, and correcting for the encroachment of the seas in the southern hemisphere, it was determined that there were 395 craters 20 miles or greater on the hidden side compared to 227 on our side. By counting the small seas it was also determined that there were four or five small maria like Mare Crisium, Mare Marginus, Mare Smythii, Mare Humboltianum, etc.

Where to put these craters and seas was, of course, unknown

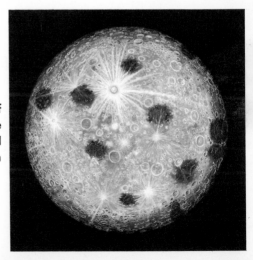

Fig. 5-10 **The statistical picture of the hidden side of the moon. The dark areas represent seas and those on the limb of the moon can be seen from our side.**

Illus.: The Decker Corp.

but with the aid of an artist this picture was constructed. In 1958 the statistical picture of the hidden side was published and in October 1959 the Lunik III pictures transmitted back to the earth showed not only the lack of a large sea complex on the hidden side, but also showed the hidden side to be quite bright indicating a region like the badlands of the southern hemisphere of our side of the moon. Precise maps of the other side of the moon may be available soon to check the results obtained from a purely statistical study.

One of the prime mysteries of the moon's surface is the ray complex so vividly seen at full moon. Tycho is the focus of a spectacular ray system. At full moon a series of bright radial streaks can be seen stretching from the crater to various distances. One ray, moving northward, cuts across the entire moon and actually disappears beyond the limb after traveling a distance of almost 2000 miles.

One of the authors has completed a project in determining the magnitude of the Tychonian ray system and has measured the rays as covering 0.45 million square miles. From the volume of material blasted from the crater, he has determined that the average depth of the rays is 18.5 feet. Immediately surrounding the crater the thickness is about 50 feet and this tapers off to 15 feet at 20° from the crater where the thickness again begins to increase.

What are the rays? Dr. John A. O'Keefe has indicated that meteoroidal impacts on the moon may have given rise to explosions which not only scattered the blasted material over the moon but also melted and shaped the material into small globules. Glass particles of this shape would reflect light like a beaded, movie-projection screen and could explain the variation in brightness with phase.

What lies on the surface of the moon? A vigorous debate has arisen among astronomers of rare competence. Some believe the dust layer on the surface may be over one-half mile thick. Others believe the dust layer may range from a fraction of an inch to perhaps a yard. The latter group also shows that solar radiations would cement the dust into a weak, semiporous material capable of supporting a human being.

Loose dust presents a frightening prospect. When a rocket motor fires to permit touchdown on the moon, the rocket exhaust will blow the dust across the rugged moonscape and the space ship may never land upright. The greatest hazard will come at the instant of touchdown. Any malfunction at this time in the early stages of lunar exploration will bring disaster to the expedition. A precise determination of the thickness and condition of the dust layer is a task of highest priority.

The question of water on the moon becomes of paramount importance because of its necessity to the perpetuation of life once the astronaut reaches the moon. In the past the authors have indicated that water exists in the rocks on the moon as water of crystallization.* Water could be baked from the rocks which could then be broken up into oxygen and hydrogen to yield an atmosphere and hydrogen for fuel. However, the presence of emitted gases indicating that the subsurface layer of the moon may be hot in some areas gives rise to suggestion that water in the liquid state may also be present there.

Dr. Zdenek Kopal indicates that water may have been present in the primordial material that gave rise to the planets and satellites of the solar system. As proof, he points out that in some meteorites we find one pound of water for every 1000 pounds of meteorite. The presence of water in this material, while surprising, is not unexpected, for both oxygen and hydrogen have always been quite abundant in the universe.

It is believed that heat from radioactive sources on the moon created temperatures high enough to expel the water molecules from the rock crystals and drive the water outward through breaks and fissures to the surface. It is considered likely that the center of the moon is completely devoid of water, whereas the crust should have a high water content.

* I. M. Levitt, *Target For Tomorrow* (New York: Fleet Publishing Co.), 1959, D. M. Cole, *Lunar Colonization* (The Martin Company), 1959.

Radio frequency studies of the lunar surface reveal that at a depth of about one yard the temperature is about −40° F. This means that even if water came up as hot steam it must condense into a liquid which then freezes into ice before reaching the surface. Along fissures the formation of ice may have taken place close to the surface, giving rise to the possibility of glaciers just beneath the surface.

Another possibility is that at one time hot geysers existed on the moon. If this action took place away from direct sunlight, the water would immediately turn to ice. If it did freeze then, the rate of sublimation is so low that in 4.5 billion years only a 160-foot sheet would disappear.

It is possible to draw some interesting conclusions as to the maximum depth of water on the moon. We know that if the terrestrial oceans were spread over a levelled earth the waters would be 6000 feet deep. Using this figure and the mass of the earth, we find that for every 50 tons of earth we have six pounds of water. By using this ratio on the moon, Dr. Kopal finds that if the same conditions existed on the moon it would be covered with a layer of water 1000 feet deep! As this water is below the surface and exists, at least in part, as ice, it cannot escape and we are forced to conclude that there is a vast volume of water on the moon. If the first explorers on the moon are fortunate, they may immediately find one of the most critical commodities needed to sustain their life.

CHAPTER 6

The Sun's Family

THE THING WE have most of in space is space itself. Only when we begin examining closely the make-up of the solar system do we appreciate the paucity of material in space. We discussed the earth-moon system and know that the system is about 93,000,000 miles from the sun. Between the earth and the sun and beyond the earth, other planets are to be found. This might lead one to suspect that our part of space is densely populated. To be sure, it is densely populated when we compare the vicinity of the earth with the remainder of the universe. It is only when we travel far from the sun that we realize that the sum total of matter in the solar system represents an infinitesimal speck in this universe.

The earth is one of a family of nine planets which revolve around the sun. In addition to the nine planets, 31 moons and a great deal of debris are found in the solar system. The debris, although of insignificant mass, when it comes close to the earth and sun may give rise to spectacular celestial displays. The solar system also contains comets and the remains of a planet which once circled the sun between Mars and Jupiter. These objects we call the *asteroids* or *planetoids*—the little planets. Permeating space is a

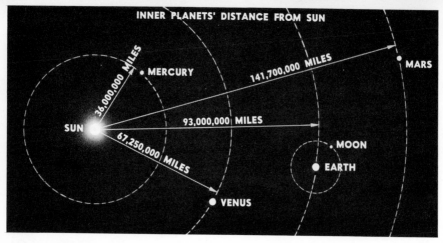

Fig 6-1 Inner planets' distance from sun.

tremendous volume of tiny, low-mass particles which are so small as to float down to the surface of the earth where they can be built up into layers in our seas.

To see the solar system in its proper perspective with respect to space, we might think of the sun as being situated in Times Square in New York. If we then considered the nearest star—Proxima Centauri—to be in San Francisco, then the earth, which would be slightly smaller than a period on this page, would be about 48 feet from the sun and the farthest planet from the sun—Pluto—would be slightly more than one-third of a mile from the sun. In the entire United States we would find only two cities to represent stars and these would be at opposite ends of the country and the planetary system surrounding the sun would be composed of tiny specks and contained in a one-mile cube. Thus we see that the stars are really isolated bodies and between them is interstellar space with perhaps a single molecule in the volume of a matchbox.

Though there are many ways in which the planets can be divided, very roughly we might say that there is one grouping which appears logical. The planets Mercury, Venus, Earth and Mars are the inner planets; the others, Jupiter, Saturn, Uranus, Neptune and Pluto, are the outer planets. We could also speak of terrestrial ones and major ones but the division is artificial, without real significance. The positions of the planets with respect to the sun permit us to discuss them in an orderly fashion. For this reason we will detail the characteristics of each planet beginning with Mercury and ending with Pluto.

MERCURY

Mercury is the smallest planet in the solar system and the closest to the sun. Roughly, its distance from the sun is about one-third that of the earth and for this reason receives about nine times as much energy from the sun as does the earth. Because of its nearness to the sun, the planet surface must be a good bit hotter. Actually, astronomers have measured the surface temperature of Mercury and find that directly beneath the sun the temperature rises to about 780 degrees Fahrenheit. Since the orbit of Mercury is highly eccentric, it means that at times it is farther from the sun at which time the temperature of the sub-solar point may drop to about 650 degrees Fahrenheit.

Astronomers believe that a long time ago this planet was in a plastic state and the tidal action of the sun pulled out a tidal bulge. When the material congealed, the gravitational field of the sun captured the bulge of the planet and constrained it always to keep the same side toward the sun. Thus one side of Mercury is hot, always facing the sun, whereas the other side is very cold, never

Fig. 6-2 Outer planets' distance from sun.

Illus.: The Decker Corp.

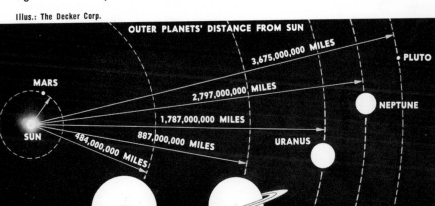

receiving radiation from the sun. Mercury librates; that is, it oscillates about its axis of rotation because of the eccentricity of its orbit. Due to the librations, almost two-thirds of its surface receives sunlight at one time or another. There are points near the poles of the planet where the sun is quite low and the moderate temperatures at these places will permit a human being to live without elaborate air conditioning equipment. The side turned away from the sun can only be a few degrees above the absolute zero of space.

Mercury is small in diameter with a mass slightly more than one-twentieth that of the earth. These two factors mean that the gravitational pull of the planet is considerably less than that of the earth. A 200-pound man on the earth would weigh 54 pounds on Mercury—about one-quarter. For the same reasons, the velocity of escape may be as low as 2.2 miles per second. The combination of high temperatures and low escape velocity means that if Mercury ever had an atmosphere, and we believe it did at one time, that atmosphere has long since escaped and only a trace remains.

Mercury swings around the sun once in 87.97 days. This is the planet's sidereal year. However, as seen from the earth, to go from western elongation back to western elongation takes 117.88 days. This is the planet's synodic year. Mercury in its motion around the sun undergoes phases like the moon. When Mercury is behind the sun, it is seen at its full phase and is about half as big as when seen in front of the sun. When the planet lies between the earth and the sun it is in the new phase and cannot be seen. Thus in its revolution around the sun the size and phase change.

VENUS

The brightest object in the sky, with the exception of the sun and the moon, is Venus. At times its brilliance frightens the uninformed and ignorant. When Venus is a bright evening star, newspaper offices are often flooded with calls inquiring about the "new" brilliant object in the sky.

Venus is considered the earth's twin, for it is almost as big as the earth. It is 7700 miles in diameter, compared to 7927 miles for the earth. Its mass is slightly less than the earth's. A 200-pound man on the earth would weigh 172 pounds on the planet. The velocity of escape is 6.3 miles per second.

The orbit of the planet is almost circular—it possesses the smallest eccentricity in the solar system. The difference in distance from the sun, at *perihelion* and *aphelion,* is only 1.2 million miles compared to over 13 million miles for Mercury and 3 million miles for the earth.

The planet circles the sun once in 225 days. When the period of the earth is taken into account, Venus' synodic period is 584 days. Thus 584 days, or about 19 months, after the planet is farthest east of the sun and an evening star, it is once more back in the same position. This means that if it is a bright evening star in the winter, 19 months later, in the summer, it will once more be a brilliant evening star. This alternation of seasons when the planet is bright often confuses observers of the sky.

Venus is the planet of mystery. No one has ever seen its surface because it is covered by a thick cloud layer. The cloud layer is manifest in the reflecting power of the planet, for it reflects approximately 60% of the radiation that falls on it. The presence of this thick atmosphere also prevents astronomers from determining the precise rotational period of the planet. Since the advent of larger telescopes, astronomers have tried, unsuccessfully, to determine the "day" of the planet. In the past the day has been "determined" as ranging from approximately 24 hours to 225 days. A breakthrough has occurred in the determination of the rotation period of Venus. Radar studies by the Jet Propulsion laboratories using the 85-foot diameter dish of the Goldstone tracking station indicate that the day and year on Venus are almost equal. A day of about 250 earth days has been tentatively determined for Venus.

The surface temperature of the planet in the past has been a matter of speculation. At one time astronomers indicated the surface temperature might be 160°F—this would be below the boiling point of water. Recent measures made with radio telescopes consistently yielded a surface temperature of about 600°F. However, definitive results obtained with the Mariner 2 probe indicate a surface temperature of about 800°F, substantiating the microwave measures made from the earth. The probe also obtained temperature measures of the cloud layers and curiously the temperature was the same on the dark side as on the light side—about 30°F below zero.

MARS

Beyond the earth is Mars which is one of the most intriguing planets in the solar system. More is written about this planet than any other, and the reason lies in the discovery of so-called "canals" by the Italian astronomer Schiaparelli.

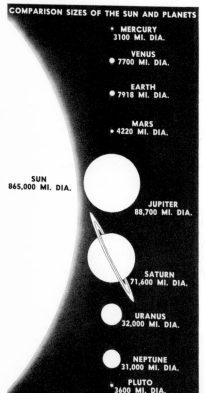

COMPARISON SIZES OF THE SUN AND PLANETS

MERCURY
3100 MI. DIA.

VENUS
7700 MI. DIA.

EARTH
7918 MI. DIA.

MARS
4220 MI. DIA.

SUN
865,000 MI. DIA.

JUPITER
88,700 MI. DIA.

SATURN
71,600 MI. DIA.

URANUS
32,000 MI. DIA.

NEPTUNE
31,000 MI. DIA.

PLUTO
3600 MI. DIA.

Fig. 6-3 Comparison sizes of the sun and planets.

Illus.: The Decker Corp.

In 1877, at the opposition of Mars, he saw strange, faint, dusky streaks at the critical limit of visibility, which means that sometimes they were visible. He called these markings *canali,* an Italian word meaning channels. Unfortunately, they were translated into English as canals and with that a fantastic volume of work went into proving and disproving their existence. The question of reality of the canals has been resolved, for skillful French astronomers using the magnificent equipment at the Pic du Midi Observatory in southern France at times of good "seeing," have observed straight line markings on the planet surface. However, on those nights when the seeing is superb, the straight line markings disintegrate into heterogenous markings indicating that the canals exist only in the minds of the observers.

Mars at times comes within 36,000,000 miles of the earth. At these close oppositions tremendous excitement is generated over the appearance of the planet. Probably this excitement is due to the image created by the layman in light of the canals which some consider the product of a superintelligence. Astronomers know that of all the other planets in the solar system Mars is the only one believed to harbor any form of life and this makes the planet so intriguing.

Mars is smaller than the earth—only 4200 miles in diameter. It possesses about one-tenth the mass of the earth and this results in a lower gravitational pull. A man weighing 200 pounds on the earth will weigh about 76 pounds on Mars. This lower gravitational pull also means that the velocity of escape from the planet is only 3.1 miles per second.

The mean distance from the sun to Mars is 142,000,000 miles, but the eccentricity of the orbit, that is, the departure from a circle, is rather large. This means that at a close opposition Mars is only 35,000,000 miles from the earth, whereas, some seven years later, Mars may be as much as 63,000,000 miles from the earth. This also accounts for the change in brightness of Mars at various oppositions. When Mars is on the other side of the sun, its distance from the earth can be as much as 248,000,000 miles.

Because Mars is farther from the sun than the earth, it circles the sun at a slower pace taking 687 days to complete its year. As seen from the earth Mars takes 780 days to go from opposition to opposition. Curiously, this synodic period is the longest of any of the planets. This lengthy period arises from the rapid motion of Mars around the sun compared to the more distant planets.

A great deal is known about Mars. We know that it possesses an atmosphere. It is not a dense atmosphere, for the surface pressure is only one pound per square inch compared to 14.7 pounds per square inch on the earth's surface. This pressure corresponds to that on the top of a 12-mile high mountain on the earth, if such a mountain existed. The atmosphere is probably nitrogen with about 4% argon. Other gases like carbon dioxide and water and, in all probability, some as yet undetected oxygen also exist there as contaminants. No direct evidence is available for oxygen; though, if Martian plants do exist, and there are cogent reasons for believing they do, then oxygen must be a by-product of the plant metabolism.

Because of the lack of an atmosphere, the temperatures on the Martian surface are severe. At the Martian equator, with the sun directly overhead, the temperature can go up to 85°F. At this same spot at night the temperature can plummet down to about 100° below zero.

Mars, like the earth, spins on its axis, but the day is about 37 minutes longer than our day. Like the earth, the axis of Mars is tipped 25° to its path around the sun compared to the 23½° for the earth. Thus Mars has seasons but the seasons on Mars are twice the length of terrestrial ones because of the longer years.

With the seasons comes the wave of vegetation which sweeps down from the poles with a speed of about 25 miles per day. Although other explanations have been offered for the wave of color seen as both green and brown by observers, it is difficult to imagine anything which would behave in this fashion except vegetation.

One of the most interesting features of the red planet is the presence of its two tiny moons which were discovered by Asaph Hall in 1877. The inner moon, Phobos, is only 3700 miles above the surface of the planet and circles the planet once in seven hours, 39 minutes. Phobos actually circles the planet three times during the course of the day. This is the only moon in the solar system that rises in the west and sets in the east as seen from the planet.

The other moon, Deimos, is five miles in diameter compared to the ten-mile diameter of Phobos. It is about 12,500 miles above the surface and circles the planet once in 30 hours, 18 minutes.

JUPITER

Beyond Mars lies the giant of the solar system—Jupiter. There is a gap in the planetary distances, for Mars is only 1½ times as far from the sun as the earth is, whereas Jupiter is five times as distant. Actually there may have been another planet in this gap in the past, and later we shall explore this possibility. Let's examine the physical characteristics of this major planet.

Jupiter has an equatorial diameter of 88,800 miles, whereas the polar diameter is about 6000 miles less. Thus we can readily see that this planet is much larger than the earth. In fact, Jupiter is larger than all the other planets combined.

The tremendous size of the planet and its great mass combine to give it a surface gravitational attraction 2.64 times that of the earth. A 200-pound man on the earth would weigh 528 pounds on the surface of Jupiter, if indeed there were a solid surface with the dimension indicated. Because of the oblateness of the planet, one would weigh 15% more at the poles than at the equator.

Jupiter is oblate because it is spinning rapidly on its axis. The day on Jupiter is nine hours, 55 minutes. This rotational period is determined by watching the features of the planets as they move as a result of the planet's rotation. The period is not a simple one for, like the sun, Jupiter also has different rotational rates as we move away from the equator. The farther from the equator, the slower the planet rotates. As Jupiter is five times as distant as the

earth from the sun, it circles the sun slowly and leisurely. The
Jovian year is about 12 earth years in length.

As seen with a telescope, Jupiter shows tremendous detail in the
form of cloud belts forming the visible surface. Again we have
never seen the surface of the planet. Spectroscopic studies indicate
that the atmosphere is composed primarily by hydrogen and helium
with methane and ammonia as impurities. Because of Jupiter's
great distance from the sun, the temperature on top of the cloud
belts is —200°F. At this temperature, most of the ammonia would
be frozen and the methane is present as a gas.

Just how far down this gaseous envelope extends is impossible
to determine observationally; only models can be formulated. The
model proposed by Dr. Rupert Wildt indicates that the planet has
a rather small core with the atmosphere tens of thousands of miles
thick. Curiously, the pressure at the bottom of this tremendous
layer of atmosphere creates a high temperature. Some astronomers
have speculated that the temperature is so high as to melt the rock
surfaces and turn them into oceans of lava.

Galileo, more than 300 years ago, discovered the four large
moons of Jupiter which are still called the Galilean moons. These
moons are comparable to our moon in size and are easily seen

Fig. 6-4 Four of the outer planets.
Illus.: Mt. Wilson and Mt. Palomar Observatories

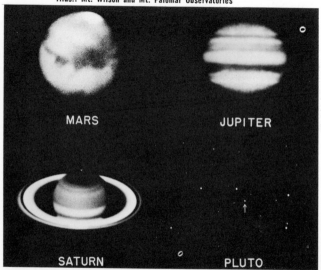

MARS   JUPITER

SATURN   PLUTO

with binoculars. Since the time of Galileo, eight others have been discovered. The twelfth was discovered by Dr. Seth B. Nicholson in 1951.

SATURN

Beyond Jupiter lies the most distant member of the solar system known to the ancients. Saturn was the slowest moving and thus the most venerated of the planets. It, too, became an intriguing object to the early telescopic observers of the night sky. Galileo with his crude telescope saw something most unusual about the planet. It appeared as though there were some appendages on each side. About 50 years later, Christian Huygens determined the true nature of the planet. Huygens discovered that Saturn was surrounded by a unique ring system. Somewhat later, Giovanni Cassini found a division in the rings which is still known as the Cassini division.

Saturn is also one of the giants of the solar system, with an equatorial diameter of about 75,000 miles. Because it, too, rotates rapidly—the day is ten hours, 14 minutes at the equator—the polar diameter is only 68,000 miles. Like Jupiter, it too has a slower rotation period as we move away from the equator.

Saturn is about ten times as distant from the sun as the earth and the year on Saturn is 29½ earth years. In the Saturnian year, the ring system which is inclined to the path around the sun by 28° goes through a type of phase which makes the ring system almost invisible twice during this period. When the rings are turned edge-on, as viewed from the earth, they can be seen only with the largest telescopes.

Like Jupiter, Saturn is completely covered by cloud belts. Again these are clouds of hydrogen, helium, methane and ammonia. The temperature on the tops of the cloud belts on Saturn is −240°F. and at this temperature most of the ammonia is in a frozen state. The methane layers are also thicker.

In addition to the rings, Saturn has a system of nine moons which can be seen and photographed.

URANUS

The first planet discovered since ancient days was Uranus, found by William Herschel in 1781 in his systematic search of the sky. This planet is about 19 times as distant from the sun as is the earth and at this distance its year is 84 earth years. It can be seen with a moderate-sized telescope as a small greenish disk.

The small size is merely an indication of its great distance from the earth. The diameter of this planet is 29,300 miles. Like all planets it spins on its axis and the day is ten hours, 45 minutes long. Again the rapid rotation has given rise to a flattening of the poles of the planet so that the polar diameter is about one-fourteenth that of the equator.

The curious feature of the planet is that the axis of rotation is "lying down." The inclination of the equator to the plane of its orbit is 98° so that we might consider the axial rotation retrograde as compared to the planets. One curious result of this position of the axis is that the planet has seasons but they are 21 years long, because it alternately presents its equator and poles to the sun with this period.

Uranus has five moons, the fifth and latest discovered by Dr. Gerard Kuiper in 1948.

NEPTUNE

The discovery of Uranus sparked a revolution in one facet of astronomy called *celestial mechanics*. After its discovery, astronomers plotted its path and were surprised to find that Uranus did not move precisely as was predicted. Continuous computations were made taking into account the perturbative effects of all the other planets, but still Uranus was not where it was supposed to be. When the errors became too great, astronomers reluctantly came to the conclusion that the reason for the discrepancy was the presence of another planet beyond Uranus. The problem of finding the disturbing body was susceptible to solution.

Two astronomers, John Couch Adams, at that time an undergraduate at Cambridge, and Urbain Jean Joseph Leverrier, in

France, attacked the problem. Adams finished his task first and sent his results to the Astronomer Royal so that he could begin a search for the new planet. However, Sir George Airy lacked the proper star chart and could not undertake what was a most difficult task. Leverrier sent his results to Johann Galle at the Berlin Observatory who at that time had just come into possession of a new set of star charts. Galle, within the hour, discovered the new planet Neptune within one degree of the point indicated by Leverrier. Here was indeed a triumph of mathematical astronomy.

In size, Neptune is almost a twin of Uranus—27,700 miles in diameter. It is about 30 times as far from the sun as is the earth and its period is 165 years. Like Uranus, it too is covered by cloud belts which are principally methane. The day on Neptune is 15 hours, 48 minutes long, and with this high rotational speed the planet should be oblate. Neptune has two satellites, Triton, discovered in 1846 by William Lassell, and Nereid, by Kuiper in 1949.

After the discovery of Neptune, and its perturbative effects on Uranus, the planet Uranus still did not move precisely as it should. With the success in discovering Neptune the American astronomer Percival Lowell undertook to find if there could be another planet which was causing the erratic motion of Uranus. Lowell actually found two solutions to the problem and decided that the more probable one put the new planet in the constellation of Gemini. After a long search nothing was uncovered. However, the search was continued using other plates of the sky made with a new telescope and finally, on February 18, 1930, Clyde Tombaugh at the Lowell Observatory found a faint fifteenth-magnitude object which turned out to be the long-sought planet. It was named Pluto and is the outer-most known planet in the solar system.

PLUTO

Pluto is about 39.5 times as distant from the sun as is the earth. It is a small planet, and because of its extreme distance we do not know precisely how big it is. The best estimate is that it is about 3600 miles in diameter. It is so far from the sun that it takes 248 years to get around once. Its mass is so small it could not have perturbed either Uranus or Neptune, unless its density approaches that of osmium.

As the measured diameter of Pluto is somewhat like Triton, the large satellite of Neptune, it has been suggested with excellent reason that Pluto is really a lost moon of Neptune or even that Triton is a captured planet. Actually, the orbit of Pluto is eccentric, and at times it comes closer to the sun than Neptune.

ASTEROIDS

Between Mars and Jupiter are to be found the asteroids. These are small bodies ranging from a maximum diameter of 480 miles down to diameters of no more than one mile. The small ones are by far the most numerous. No one knows precisely how many asteroids there are. Dr. Walter Baade, using the 100-inch reflector at Mt. Wilson, estimated that there should be about 44,000 asteroids brighter than the nineteenth magnitude. Even if this number were doubled and the asteriods put together in a large ball, they would have a mass less than one-sixth that of the earth. If the combined mass were higher, they would disturb Mars in its orbit.

Following the discovery of the first asteroid Ceres, on December 31, 1801, others were found very rapidly. In March 1802, Pallas was discovered. In 1804, Juno, and in 1807, Vesta were found. By the turn of the century over 300 asteroids had been discovered. With the introduction of photography more and more were found until in the ten years between 1930 and 1939 about 2800 asteroids were discovered.

Although most of the asteroids move between the orbits of Mars and Jupiter, some orbits are quite eccentric and come well inside the earth's orbit at perihelion. One asteroid, Icarus, has the shortest period and at times dips within the orbit of Mercury.

Fig. 6-5 Halley's comet.

COMETS

As this is being written, Comet Wilson is in the sky and can be seen in the early hours of the morning. Naked-eye comets are rare, though we are perhaps visited by a dozen comets each year. A bright, naked-eye comet is a spectacular object and becomes a conversation piece for a long time.

Just what are these comets and from where do they come? The answers to these questions are most difficult. No one has ever reached out to feel a comet or examine it first hand. The only way in which these objects can be studied is by means of their light. It is from this light that astronomers interpret the history of these objects.

One of the most astute astronomers who has specialized in the study of comets is Dr. Fred L. Whipple at Harvard. His comet models have explained many of the questions posed by these objects.

A comet has been likened to a flying gravel bank. It has no solidity, only a very few particles perhaps no larger than grains of sand. However, in and around these grains are the hydrogen ices, that is, compounds of hydrogen and carbon—methane—or hydrogen and oxygen—water—or hydrogen and nitrogen—ammonia. When comets come toward the sun, its radiation boils off the ices which are then repelled by radiation pressure and the "proton wind" to form the tail.

A comet has a well-defined anatomy. The nucleus is a sharp starlike object in the head. Surrounding the nucleus is the *coma* which is dense enough to reflect sunlight, and faint stars cannot be seen through it. The material which flows back from the coma forms the tail of the comet. This is a thin, tenuous gas which is excited and made to glow by the radiation of the sun. Stars can be seen through the tail of the comet.

It is the tail of the comet which makes the comet a spectacular object. It may develop into long, thin streamers tens of millions of miles in length and when seen from the earth may cover an angular distance in excess of 90°. Photographs have shown that the tail undergoes curious transformations; knots and bulges form and dissipate in short periods of time.

Astronomers do not know how many comets there are, but they believe that interstellar space to a distance of several light years represents a reservoir or deep freeze where comets lie dormant. The passing of a star at several light-years from the sun may disturb the comet to make it susceptible to the gravitational field of the sun which attracts it. In coming in toward the sun the cometary orbit is perturbed by the major planets so that, in general, the period is considerably shortened. This means that the comet comes in again and again until finally its substance is dissipated and it ceases to be a comet.

CHAPTER 7

Motions and Positions In Space

W E HAVE BEEN discussing the members of the solar system, describing them, detailing their physical characteristics and, indeed, their peculiarities. These bodies all have something in common: they move.

Motion in our universe is a quality which is inherent in almost everything we see. Nothing stands still. Only when we consider the motions of these bodies do we begin to appreciate how dynamic this universe really is. Curiously, it is these motions which provide some of the answers to questions posed about objects we see in the sky. It is apparent that if motion were taken away from these objects they would instantly become mysterious bodies to us.

For example, because the moon moves around the earth and this motion can be precisely measured, we determine the mass of the moon and from that other physical characteristics. Because the planets circle the sun we can determine their physical characteristics, which is also true of the satellites of the planets. In the case of stars, the motions involved in a double-star group permit us to determine their characteristics. Although these characteristics are only in terms of the sun, the gap in knowledge concerning these systems has narrowed considerably.

Thus we see that motion represents one of the most significant characteristics of a celestial body; and this is no less true of man-made objects which are launched as satellites and probes. These, in the strictest sense of the word—when they have escaped from the earth—become celestial objects.

LAWS OF MOTION

We see the sun, moon, planets and other objects moving in the sky. Some of these bodies appear to move erratically, like the comets, and others, like the planets, move in paths which are almost precisely describable. How do astronomers go about finding out how these bodies move and how to predict their future positions?

Actually, all of the motions of celestial objects are governed by rather few laws. Kepler, in the beginning of the 17th century, enunciated his three laws of planetary motion, and following him Newton provided the other essential laws to describe accurately the motions of the celestial objects. Once these laws had been derived, scientists could undertake furnishing definitive descriptions of the motions of planets and providing information concerning their future positions.

The genius that provided these first laws of planetary motion, Johann Kepler, was an ingenious, sensitive young man who became the pupil of Tycho Brahe, the greatest observational astronomer in the history of pre-telescopic astronomy. It is doubtful that Isaac Newton could have arrived at his laws of motion and of gravitation, or even the invention of the calculus, without the foundation laid by Kepler. In fact, many scientists believe that Kepler was on the verge of stating all of them just before his death in 1630.

From the wealth of observational data provided by Tycho, Kepler chose to investigate Mars for a definitive answer to the question of the motions of this body. Only when Kepler discarded the idea that the planets move in "perfect" curves, that is, circles, did the answer come to him. In 1609 he announced his first and second laws of planetary motion, and by 1618 the third of the unifying laws had been established. Historians who have studied the work of this man indicate that to arrive at these laws he made innumerable guesses and took six years of tedious, incessant calculation.

As we know the laws today they state:

1. Each planet moves in an ellipse which has the sun at one of its foci.
2. The radius vector of each planet passes over equal areas in equal intervals of time.
3. The cubes of the mean distances of any two planets from the sun are to each other as the squares of their periods.

The first law tells us that the orbit of any planet around the sun is an ellipse. In the case of the earth, the sun is not in the center but removed 1,500,000 miles from the center at one focus of the ellipse. Thus in early July the earth is 94,500,000 miles away from the sun, whereas in early January it is 91,500,000 miles away.

The second law indicates that when the earth is close to the sun it must travel faster than when it is farther away. When the earth is nearest to the sun, at perihelion, its speed is 18.8 miles

Fig. 7-1 Kepler's First Law.

Illus.: The Decker Corp.

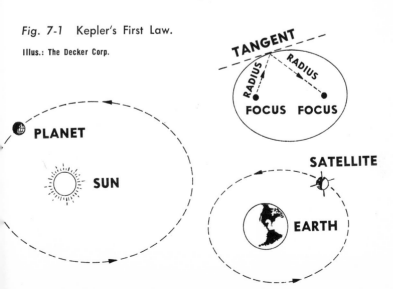

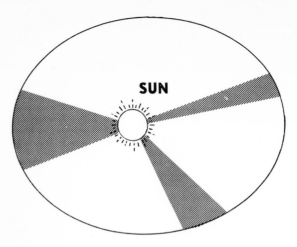

Fig. 7-2 Law of Equal Areas.

Illus.: The Decker Corp.

per second, whereas at aphelion the speed is 18.2 miles per second. At the mean distance, the speed of the earth is 18.5 miles per second. Thus the difference in speeds at perihelion and aphelion is only 0.6 miles per second. Another way of looking at this is that when the earth is closer to the sun, the gravitational pull of the sun is greater and to keep from falling into the sun the earth must travel faster. When the earth is traveling faster, the radius vector—the line joining the centers of the earth and sun— is shorter. To sweep over the same area in an equivalent length of time it must sweep faster, as indicated in Figure 7-2.

To illustrate the third law, let's examine Pluto and Mercury. Pluto's distance from the sun is close to 100 times Mercury's— we are rounding off the figures for the purpose of better understanding. Pluto's period of revolution—its year—is almost 250 years; Mercury's period is about one-quarter year. Pluto's period, then, is about 1000 times that of Mercury. If we square the ratio of the periods, we get 1,000,000. When we cube the ratio of distances we get 100 × 100 × 100, which also equals 1,000,000. Thus, knowing the period of Pluto, we could have found its distance or vice versa.

Other laws of motion were discovered by two of the greatest experimental scientists who ever lived. Galileo, by diligent experimentation, had arrived at empirical laws of motion which Newton extended and formalized in later years as his three laws of motion, which have already been discussed.

Once the tools for determining past, present and future positions of celestial objects were available, it remained for astronomers to use them. It must be realized that astronomers understood the laws of motion but their application to specific problems remained obscure. There was, for instance, no accurate method of computing the orbit of a body which moved around the sun. It is true that Halley traced the comet named for him back over many apparitions and he predicted the coming return. It is also true that Lagrange and Laplace scored phenomenal successes in the understanding of celestial motions. However, predictions from very few observations of an object taken at short intervals were still beyond astronomy. What could be done was to determine from its period its mean distance from the sun. Newton also showed that all the bodies through their gravitational interactions affected the motions of other bodies. In Chapter 5 it was indicated that the moon undergoes many erratic motions. Newton had been able to explain the action of all of these. But the precise mechanism whereby future position from observations of a celestial body could be determined was not yet completely understood.

It remained until the first day of the 19th century for this important breakthrough to materialize.

ORBITAL CHARACTERISTICS

On January 1, 1801, the Sicilian astronomer Professor Guiseppe Piazzi, of Palermo, observed a "star" in the constellation of Taurus which did not appear on the charts he possessed. The following night he saw that the small, eighth-magnitude star had shifted its position. By January 24, he was convinced that what he was observing was not a star and as it had to be a member of the solar system, it must necessarily be a comet. Piazzi wrote to two astronomers telling them of his discovery. By February 11 he was taken ill and he was unable to continue observing the object. His letters to the other astronomers did not get to them until it was too late to continue observing the object and thus it appeared that the "star" would be lost. Those mathematical astronomers who tried to calculate an orbit for the object were handicapped because the observations were too close together and too few. Thus, while they could make calculations, they could not determine a definitive orbit for the body so that they might once more institute a search for it.

At that time there lived in Germany one of the greatest mathematicians the world has ever known. At the age of 24 Carl Friedrich Gauss had developed some powerful mathematical tools. These tools he applied to Piazzi's observations and computed an orbit for the object. He predicted the position of the object and on December 31, 1801 Baron Von Zach rediscovered the object near the point Gauss had indicated. The "star" was called Ceres and marked the discovery of the first asteroid.

The significant point was not that the asteroid was rediscovered but that Gauss had developed a sound, precise method for predicting future positions of celestial objects and in doing so laid the groundwork for the study of an important branch of astronomy we today call celestial mechanics.

In this way, the pieces of the puzzle were being assembled so that present-day scientists can put probes and satellites into the sky and know their precise motions and their behavior.

To predict position and motion it is necessary to establish an orbit for the body in question. When the orbit is established, it indicates the path of the body and this in turn permits us to find the body at any given time. The orbit of any celestial object is defined by certain parameters called the elements of the orbit. These and their descriptions are:

a) the semi-major axis of the orbital ellipse, or the mean distance of the object from the sun; this determines the size of the orbit and the period of revolution. When the orbit is not closed as in a parabolic one, q is used to denote the closest approach to the sun or the perihelion distance.

e) the eccentricity or ellipticity of the orbit; this with a determines the shape of the orbit and the distance from the center to the focus. The eccentricity can vary from zero for a circle with no eccentricity to values near unity for highly eccentric orbits. It is unity for parabolic orbits and greater than unity for hyperbolic orbits.

i) the inclination of the plane of the orbit with respect to a reference plane. This can be the tilt of the orbit with respect to the earth's plane or ecliptic. In the case of an artificial satellite this is the tilt which the plane of the satellite orbit makes with the earth's equator. In the case of a planet the reference orbit is taken as the plane of the ecliptic.

Ω) the longitude of the ascending node of the orbit, or the point on the ecliptic where the body crosses the ecliptic from south to north; this determines the direction of the tilt of the orbit or the position of the orbital plane in space. This angle is measured toward the east in the reference plane from the vernal equinox.

ω) the argument of perihelion, which is the angular distance from the ascending node, measured along the body's orbital plane, to the perihelion point; this reveals the position of the orbital ellipse in its plane. Sometimes Ω and ω are added together and called π, the longitude of perihelion.

T) the time of perihelion passage, the statement of the moment when the body is exactly nearest the sun. From this one statement of the position of the body in its orbit at a certain time, its position in its orbit at any other time can be determined.

P) the sidereal period. The time it takes the planet to circle the sun with respect to stellar background.

All these concepts of motion of a planet around the sun can be transferred to problems of motions of satellites around the earth, with only a few minor changes. We speak of perigee, that point in the orbit where the satellite makes its closest approach to the

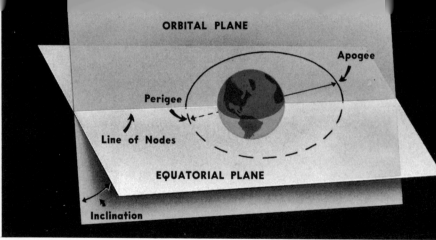

Fig. 7-3 Satellite orbit characteristics.

Illus.: The Decker Corp.

earth, instead of perihelion. The ascending node is the place where the satellite crosses the equator on its northward motion. The other parameters have been identified when listed. Just as these elements identify the orbit of a planet moving around the sun, these same elements describe the orbit of a satellite around the earth.

SATELLITE VELOCITY

There are many relations which can be derived from rather simple formulas governing the behavior of a satellite around the earth. Assuming that the satellite is injected into the precise orbit, the scientists can determine the period and the speed of the satellite. If the orbit is highly eccentric, the speed of the satellite will vary greatly at perigee and apogee. If the satellite orbits the earth in a circular orbit, the speed throughout the orbit will be constant.

The satellite velocity in a circular orbit can be expressed in the simple formula:

$$V^2 = \frac{gR^2}{R + h} \text{ *}$$

* The satellite velocity in a general orbit is given by

$$V^2 = gR^2 \left(\frac{2}{R + h} + \frac{1}{a} \right)$$

where a = semi-major axis of the orbit

where V = velocity in orbit
  g = value of gravity at earth's surface
  R = radius of the earth
  h = altitude above surface of the earth

The period of a satellite is equal to the circumference of the orbit divided by the velocity.

$$P = \frac{2\pi\,(R+h)}{V} = \frac{2\pi\,(R+h)^{3/2}}{\sqrt{g}\,R}$$

Figure 7-4 can be used to demonstrate this relationship. The announced period for Sputnik I was 96 minutes, and the apogee was given as 550 miles. From the graph we find that a period of 96 minutes gives an average altitude of 350 miles. Since the apogee was 200 miles greater than this average, the perigee must have been 200 less or 150 miles.

The period of Sputnik II was 103.5 minutes, the apogee was 1050 miles. The mean altitude for that period is 575 miles, which is 475 miles less than the announced apogee, hence perigee is 575 less 475 or 100 miles. The announced perigee was 104 miles.

For Explorer I, the lowest altitude was announced as 230 miles, the highest as 1600 miles. The mean altitude is 915 miles. The period corresponding to this altitude is 115 minutes. As the altitude increases, the period increases until, when an altitude of 22,300 miles is attained, the period is precisely the rotational period of the earth. If a satellite is launched from the equator at this altitude, it will remain stationary over a given point on the earth's surface. Orbits like these are called *synchronous orbits*.

SATELLITE VISIBILITY

The range of visibility of a satellite, or the area of the earth seen from the satellite, can be computed in the following manner (see Figures 7-5 and 7-6):

where D = the position of the satellite at altitude h
  C = the center of the earth
  R = the radius of the earth (3960 miles)

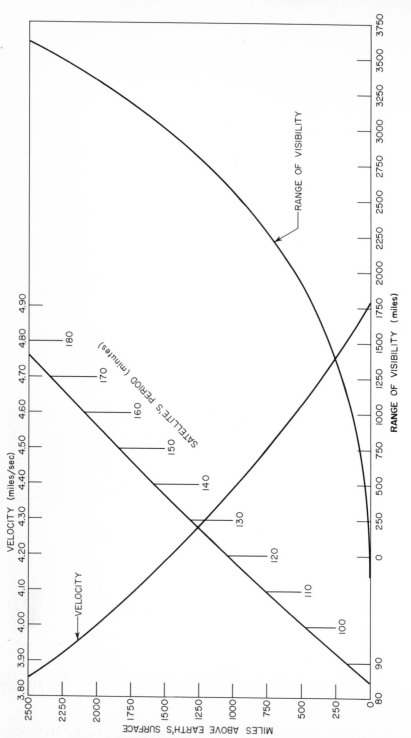

Fig. 7-4 Relationships between velocity, period, altitude, and visibility of earth satellites.

AEB = arc of earth's surface visible from D

$\cos ACD = AC/CD$

However, $AC = R$ and $CD = R + h$. Thus,

$$\cos ACD = \frac{R}{R + h}$$

By assigning values to h, it is possible to compute the corresponding values of angle ACD.

Using Explorer I as an example, we find that at its maximum altitude of 1600 miles the range of visibility is 3075 miles; the total visible arc of the earth's surface is twice this, or 6150 miles. When Explorer I was closest to the earth, at an altitude of 230 miles, the range of visibility was only 1300 miles, the total arc 2600 miles.

Fig. 7-6 Areas of earth visible from satellites at different altitudes.

Fig. 7-5

Illus.: The Decker Corp.

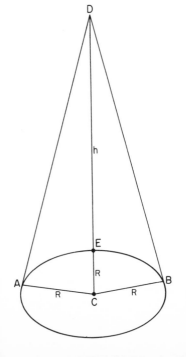

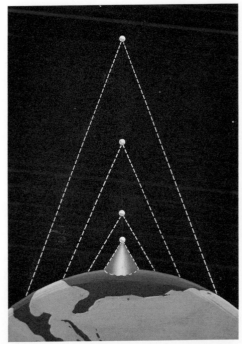

PECULIARITIES OF SATELLITE ORBITS

The foregoing are initial satellite altitudes. A sensible atmosphere exists even above 150 miles altitude, and each time the satellite moves through its perigee it experiences a resistance or drag. This robs the satellite of some of its kinetic energy and reduces the perigeal velocity. The immediate effect of this drag is to permit gravity to pull the satellite closer to the earth's surface. This effect shows up most strongly at apogee so that drag tends to "circularize" the orbit. As the satellite moves in a smaller orbit, its average speed increases accordingly and its period is shortened. Finally, when the period falls below 90 minutes, the satellite will spiral rapidly toward the earth and be incinerated on its way down by the friction with the earth's denser lower atmosphere.

To this point we have neglected the important fact that the earth is an oblate spheroid and that its mass is not all concentrated at its center. The equatorial diameter of the earth is about 27 miles greater than the polar diameter. This equatorial bulge perturbs the satellite in its motion around the earth. If the satellite moved exactly parallel to the earth's equator all the way around, there would be no such disturbance.

There is a slow advance of the perigee point of the satellite which means the orbit is non-reentrant and the orbit does not retrace itself each time. The perigee point moves along the orbit with a speed that is determined by its altitude. For an equatorial satellite orbit with an average height of 500 miles, the perigee point completes a circuit of the orbit in about 55 days.

The equatorial bulge of the earth produces a regression of the nodes of the orbit. The plane of the orbit, while maintaining the same inclination, or tilt, changes the direction of the tilt, like a top whose axis traces out a cone as it spins.

If a satellite is launched in the plane of the equator, the equatorial bulge of the earth will affect the orbit of the satellite a maximum amount. A satellite launched in a polar orbit will experience a zero precessional effect. At intermediate latitudes the effect will be proportional to the cosine of the inclination.

Another significant point about satellite orbits is that they move in paths determined by the geometry of launching. From the Cape Canaveral launching grounds, a rocket aimed due east (to take advantage of the earth's rotation) will move in a path which goes from 28½° north to 28½° south. The satellite orbit can never have an inclination of less than 28½°. If the satellite is fired south and east to make an angle of 34° with the equator, the satellite will pass overhead at latitudes 34° both south and north. If the rocket is aimed directly north or south, the satellite can be put into a polar orbit.

With the prospect of synchronous communications satellites it is desirable to put them over the equator. To do this means that these satellites must be fired from the equator or, if these equatorial launching sites are unavailable, satellites will have to be "dog-legged" into an equatorial orbit.

POSITION IN THE SKY

We have indicated that objects in the sky all have one thing in common: they move. Because they move it means that we who observe these motions must have some means of identifying the motion against the background of the sky or stars. Thus we must become acquainted with the terminology used by astronomers in their description of the positions of celestial objects.

Astronomers have found it convenient to picture all heavenly bodies as being positioned on a sphere with an infinite radius whose center is the eye of the observer. The position of an object on the sphere is on a line through the eye of the observer and the object. With this type of presentation, angular distances between points and angles between planes can readily be solved by application of the formulae of spherical trigonometry.

Although every observer has a different celestial sphere, actually, our difference of position on the earth is so small with respect to the distances of most celestial objects that we can always assume the centers of the various spheres to be coincident. Only when we are concerned with satellites whose distances are small do we have to make corrections for position on the earth.

Now let's correlate the systems we use in the sky with those used on earth.

Look at a globe of the earth. You will find there a skeleton of lines that indicate two coordinates—*latitude* and *longitude*. With the aid of these lines, the coordinates, and thus the position, of a feature, can be determined.

The circles which run north and south through the poles are called *meridians of longitude;* those parallel to the equator are called *parallels of latitude.* The starting point for indicating latitude is the equator; we can count 90° both north and south.

The arbitrary longitudinal starting point, or zero degrees longitude, is the meridian that passes through Greenwich, England, a surburb of London. We measure longitude both eastward and westward for 180° from this prime meridian.

Just as a location on the earth can be identified by naming its latitude and longitude, so objects in the sky can be located by the use of two similar coordinates. Someone might say, "I saw a very bright star in the southwest, about halfway up in the sky." Here the two coordinates employed are the direction as applied to the points of the compass and the altitude or angle of the object above the horizon.

This system, based on compass direction and altitude, and using the horizon as the base circle, is called the *altitude-azimuth* system, or, more commonly, the *altazimuth* system. The *altitude* is measured from the horizon upward through 90° to the zenith, the overhead point. The *azimuth* is measured through 360° from north on the horizon, through the east, south and west. A line drawn through the object from the horizon to the zenith is called the *vertical circle* of the object. Thus, if we measure the azimuth from the north point eastward until we come to the foot of the vertical circle through an object where it cuts the horizon, we will know the location of the object.

The altitude and azimuth of an object change with time. Consider the sun, for example, which to the observer has an altitude of zero at sunrise and sunset, and which gradually increases its altitude throughout the morning and decreases it throughout the afternoon. Its azimuth, too, changes. Sunrise takes place on the eastern horizon and sunset takes place in the west. At noon, in the northern hemisphere (except very close to the equator) the sun is in the south; at noon in the southern hemisphere it is in the north.

The sun, the moon and the stars appear to be changing their altitudes and azimuths constantly with time. There is a system of coordinates, however, in which the stars in particular retain nearly fixed positions for considerable periods of time. This is known as the *equatorial system* and is essentially a transference of our terrestrial latitude-longitude system to the sky.

Whereas the terrestrial equator is the fundamental circle in the mapping of the earth, in the equatorial system in the sky we use the celestial equator, which is exactly over the earth's equator. Ninety degrees from the celestial equator in either direction are the celestial poles, exactly over the earth's poles. Measurements north or south from the celestial equator are called north *declination* or south declination respectively, instead of north and south latitude. Circles passing from pole to pole are called *hour circles* instead of meridians of longitude.

The starting point for counting hour circles is called the *vernal equinox*, where the sun stands at the instant of the beginning of spring. The earth's orbit is tilted $23\frac{1}{2}°$ to the earth's equator. If we project the earth's orbit against the sky, we arrive at a circle called the *ecliptic*, and the vernal equinox is one of two points where the ecliptic and celestial equator intersect.

On earth, east-west measure is made in either direction from the meridian of Greenwich. In the equatorial, or celestial system, this is called *right ascension* and is only measured eastward, all the way around the complete circle, from the hour circle passing through the vernal equinox. This coordinate is reckoned in hours, minutes and seconds.

If we know the position of an object in space, the time of day, the date and our position on earth, we can determine its direction and, thus, place it in either the equatorial or the altazimuth system, as we wish.

CHAPTER 8

The Sun

THE NEAREST STAR is only 93,000,000 miles away. While all the other stars can never be seen as more than a point of light, this star is so close that it appears as big as the full moon. When a telescope is trained on it, incredibly complex surface detail becomes apparent. Like a few other stars, this one has a name—we call it the sun. Astronomers know that if they are ever to resolve the mysteries of the stars it is necessary first to find all the answers to the questions posed about our sun.

We have a particular interest in the sun. It is the giver of life to everything on the earth. Although apparently nothing happens to us when a distant star undergoes cataclysmic changes or erupts into a nova, or new star, if the sun should ever undergo such a change, and some astronomers are certain it will at some distant future date, all life on this earth would quickly cease. If the sun should suddenly become a nova, a wave of radiation would sweep over the earth and incinerate everything and everybody on it. If the sun should pass through a very dense cloud of interstellar dust, obscuring its radiation even by a small fraction, the earth would turn into an icy graveyard. Thus we have a particular interest in a stable sun as the giver and sustainer of life on the earth.

Because the sun is so near, we know a great deal about its physical characteristics. It has been observed for millenia by inquisitive philosophers who were puzzled by this warm, vital body which rose and dropped below the horizon with a regularity that man used as a measure of time—the day. It is recorded that the Chinese in looking at the sun with the naked eye could see blemishes on it which today we call sunspots. However, it was not until optical aid was developed that the true nature of the sun became known to man. Until that time there were curious notions as to its behavior.

As the earth was considered the center of the universe, it was believed that the sun revolved around the earth. Early Greek philosophers believed the sun to be only 35 miles in diameter and a mere 4000 miles distant. In the fourth century B.C., Aristotle taught that the sun was a ball of pure fire. In the third century B.C., Aristarchus, with no instruments, determined the solar distance as 720,000 miles. Later philosophers and scientists posited greater distances and today the sun is put at approximately 93,000,000 miles from the earth.

As this earth-sun distance is one of the most fundamental units in all of astronomy, for the distance to every object in the universe is based on this calculation, it is important that this figure be derived accurately. Only in very recent years, with the advent of man-made rocket probes which circle the sun, has this unit been derived with the precision necessary to establish our baseline.

Attempts have been made to establish the earth-sun distance by many groups over the past three centuries. David Rittenhouse, using the transit of Venus in 1769, established the distance as 93,000,000 miles—a value very close to that used today.

A more accurate value was attained using the close approach of the asteroid Eros. This small body periodically moves quite close to the earth and can be observed from many widely scattered observatories on the earth. When the many observations and results were collated, it resulted in the earth-sun distance being computed as 92,915,000, with a probable error of about 4,100 miles.

A more precise method used for this determination was the Pioneer V probe launched March 11, 1960. As this probe circled the sun, radio waves were flashed to it. The motion of the solar satellite caused a shift in the frequency of the received signal. So precise was the instrumentation that scientists could detect a shift of a single cycle in 402,000,000 cycles. The precise orbit of the probe was computed, taking into account all the perturbations caused by other members of the solar system. The astronomical unit computed by this method was determined as 92,924,900 miles, with an uncertainty of about 8,700 miles. When scientists can place probes in orbit around the sun which can broadcast over a

Fig. 8-1 Derivation of the astronomical unit with Pioneer V probe.

Illus.: General Features Corp.

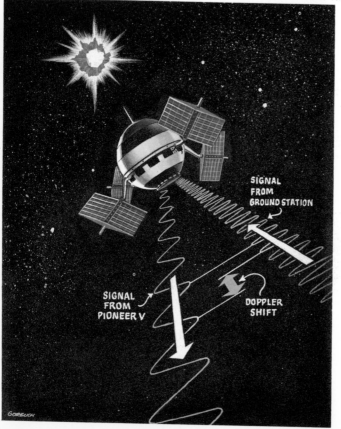

complete circuit of the sun, then it may be possible to refine these measurements and arrive at a more precise determination of the astronomical, unit using this method.

However, the foregoing is not the only method employed using radio signals. With the advent of radar, scientists began speculating on the possibility of bouncing radar signals off Venus when the planet was closest to the earth. The idea behind this method is that when the signals are bounced from Venus when it is approaching the earth the signals, returning from the planet, are "piled up" and the frequency is increased. This increase in frequency permits the precise speed of the planet to be determined and, in turn, the earth-sun distance can be found. Using Venus, the astronomical unit is computed as 92,956,300 miles, with an uncertainty of only 300 miles.

Pending the determination of a definitive value for the astronomical unit we might take the provisional value of Dr. Samuel Herrick * of 92,960,000 miles as being most representative.

Once the distance of the sun is known we can easily determine its diameter. The angular diameter of the sun can be measured with telescopes, and when this is done it is found that the sun subtends an angle of approximately one-half degree. In this way, the diameter of the sun is computed to be 865,000 miles. In actual size it is about 110 times the diameter of the earth and the volume must then be more than a million times that of the earth. If we could derive its mass, its density could also be determined.

Astronomers determine the mass of the sun by calculating its accelerating effects on the earth. If the earth suddenly stopped moving around the sun, it would begin to fall in toward the sun. Its motion toward the sun would be about one-ninth of an inch for the first second. In fact, the earth does fall this amount every second around the sun to pursue its path. We know how much the acceleration is on the earth; in the first second an object falls 16.1 feet towards the surface. Now when we take into account the

---

* Samuel Herrick, *Space Age Astronomy*, Eds., Armin J. Deutsch and Wolfgang B. Klemperer (New York: Academic Press, 1962).

inverse square law from the center of the sphere, we find that the mass of the sun is about 330,000 times that of the earth. With the mass and diameter known, the density of the sun can be computed and it comes to 1.41 times that of water. It should be realized that this is the average density. As we penetrate below the top layers of the sun the density must go higher, and it is believed that at the center of the sun the density is about 77, compared to 22.5 for the density of the most massive element, osmium.

Because of the great size and mass of the sun, it is has an intense gravitational field. A 200-pound man on the earth would weigh 28 times as much, or 5600 pounds, on the sun. By the same token, the velocity of escape is also considerably more—380 miles per second compared to seven miles per second for the earth.

Only with a telescope can detail on the sun be observed. Although a telescope can be used to project an image of the sun or to see it directly, there is one important precaution to be observed when making solar observations. The sun is so bright that there exist records of men losing their sight by looking at it. In a telescope which can pick up a great deal more light than the unaided eye it is disastrous to view the sun even for an instant. Thus solar observers use filters to cut down the intensity of the sun. Once the telescope has been fitted with a filter or a device to reduce the light to a fraction of one per cent of the incident light, observation can begin.

The surface of the sun is many things. What we see depends on the instruments used to observe the disk. When we use our naked eye and look at the sun, when it is low enough on the horizon to permit us to view it, we see the *photosphere*. This is the light-giving layer of the sun. As we shall presently discover, the only other feature to be seen at this time are sunspots, if they are large enough—that is, in excess of 25,000 miles in diameter.

When we use the telescope with the proper safeguards, we can see more detail. We notice that the center of the sun is brighter than the edge. The reason for this limb darkening is that we can see deeper into the hot layers of the sun at the center where the

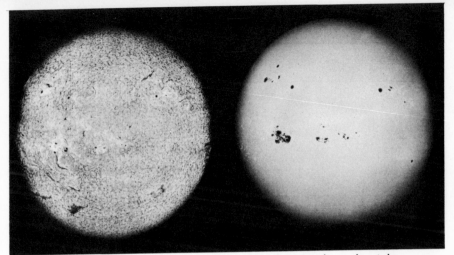

Fig. 8-2 Simultaneous pictures of the sun. The photograph on the right is the sun as seen in white light. The other is the sun seen in the red light of hydrogen.   Illus.: Mt. Wilson and Mt. Palomar Observatories

overlying solar atmosphere is thinnest. Large bright mottlings or faculae can be seen near the limb where the sun is darkest. With a large telescope, under ideal conditions, tiny granulations as small as 150 miles in diameter become visible.

With a *spectrohelioscope,* or *spectroheliograph,* a device to view or photograph the sun in light of a single wave length, in either hydrogen or calcium light, other markings can be seen or photographed. Sunspots show up rather well in these photographs, and surrounding a spot may be seen the filamentary hydrogen or calcium flocculi. At the edge of the sun may be seen hydrogen or

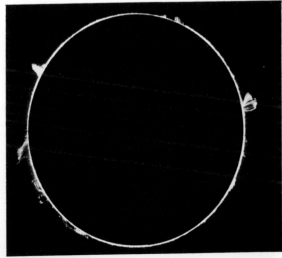

Fig 8-3 Entire outer rim of the sun showing distribution and types of prominences.

Illus.: Mt. Wilson and Mt. Palomar Observatories

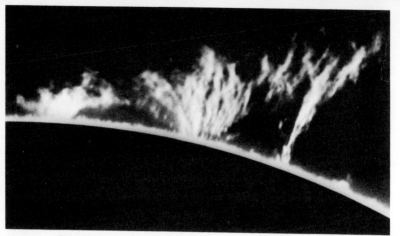

Fig. 8-4 Prominence complex on sun. The right-hand cloud extends to a height of 80,000 miles.

Illus.: Mt. Wilson and Mt. Palomar Observatories

calcium clouds, called *prominences,* projected against the black background of the sky. These are remarkable clouds which, at times, move with violent motion both to and from the sun occasionally to escape from the sun. Time lapse photography of these prominences presents some of the most thrilling pictures of nature.

At the time of a total eclipse of the sun, when the moon has completely covered the solar disk, there appears the pearly outer atmosphere of the sun—the *corona.* This outer atmosphere can be seen to extend several solar radii from the sun, and on long exposure photographs the extensions reach out to 7,000,000 miles.

The shape of the corona is influenced by sunspot activity. When sunspots are most numerous, the corona is almost concentric

Fig. 8-5 Corona of the sun photographed at the total eclipse of June 8, 1918. The corona is circular as this eclipse took place just one year after sunspot maximum.

Illus.: Mt. Wilson and Mt. Palomar Observatories

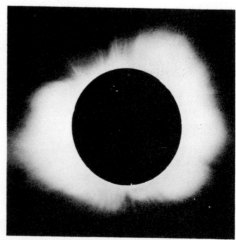

with the solar disk. At sunspot minimum the corona is irregular in shape and the extra long streamers centered on the solar equator are much in evidence.

In the covering and uncovering of the sun, at the time of a total solar eclipse, two other layers become visible. At that time the chromosphere and the reversing layers are visible.

The *reversing layer* lies on top of the photosphere and in it are contained the atoms of the various elements which steal tiny bits of energy from the radiation coming from the photosphere. The atoms pick particular bits of energy from the continuous spectrum. The lack of these bits of radiation gives rise to the dark absorption lines seen in the solar spectrum. Since each element can only take a particular bit of radiation, the resulting lines permit astronomers to identify the elements in the solar atmosphere. About 70 of the 92 known stable elements have been found there.

The *chromosphere* lies on top of the reversing layer. It has a reddish appearance due to abundance of hydrogen in the solar atmosphere and the strongest line in the spectrum of this gas is red. It is a thin layer as seen from the earth but it is still 10,000 miles thick. It is from this layer that prominences shoot up from the surface.

In a radio telescope the sun has still a different appearance. A radio telescope sees the sun as an enormous object 20 times the diameter of the sun we see. With a 10° diameter, the radio sun is 400 times the area of the visual sun. In tracking with the radio telescope, different portions of the sun, as we move away from the limb, emit different radio signals over a wide range of frequencies. This branch of astronomy is still in its infancy.

The features almost always seen on the sun are dark markings called *sunspots*. There are times when we can observe the sun for as long as a month without seeing one, but in most cases these markings will be present. As we noted earlier, these were first observed by the Chinese. After Galileo used his telescope on the sun, scientists became quite conscious of these markings. Spots can last a long time—one persisted for 18 months, whereas others may last

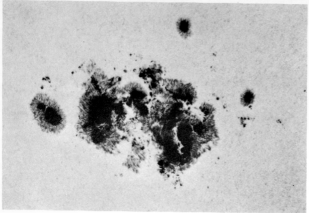

just long enough to be seen and recorded. Size apparently has a great deal to do with longevity. In general the larger a spot the longer it will persist.

Let's imagine we are observing the sun when spots are numerous. Spots can occur singly or in clusters. Most often they occur in pairs, or perhaps a better description is pairs of clusters. If we choose a single large spot and examine it carefully, we see a dark central core or *umbra* with no obvious structure. Surrounding the central core is the *penumbra*. The penumbra is a grayish area made up of filaments. It is as though the bright areas encroached over the umbra in thin, long streaks to give it a gray shade. This encroachment is the penumbra.

It is important to point out that the completely dark umbra is not uniformly dark. High resolution photographs taken with the balloon-flown STRATOSCOPE cameras indicate that tiny white spots appear as though emerging from the depths of the spot.

Occasionally associated with spots are brighter areas called *faculae*. These can be seen on photographs, particularly if one examines the limb of the sun.

In the past sunspots have been regarded as centers of giant magnetic storms; current thinking considers them quiescent areas in the extraordinarily turbulent solar atmosphere. Associated with spots are intense magnetic fields which have the peculiar property of maintaining the general shape of the sunspot.

In the telescope sunspots appear black. Actually they are quite bright. The reason for the dark appearance is the filtering of the sun's light to permit solar observations. The temperature of the sunspot may be about 6000 degrees Fahrenheit, whereas the temperature of the surrounding surface is 10,800 degrees Fahrenheit. Thus, when the surface is dimmed to permit viewing, the spot, being cooler, becomes black. To get some idea of the radiation emitted by a sunspot, we might imagine that the entire sun is made up of sunspot material. The "sunspot sun" would still appear 100 times as bright as the full moon.

Sunspots come and go in cycles which average about 11⅓ years. A periodicity was apparent in the number of spots for a long time, but it remained for a German apothecary and amateur astronomer, S. H. Schwabe to determine, in 1843, the cyclical nature of sunspots, announcing a period of about ten years. Since that time, astronomers have devoted a great deal of time and study to the cyclical nature of their appearance. Today the cycle, or really double cycle, is known to be about 23 years. This 23-year period represents the time from when spots in a particular hemisphere of the sun have a certain magnetic polarity to the time when that polarity is again present.

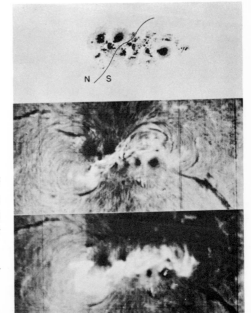

Fig. 8-7 Spectroheliograms of sun showing curve in leading and following spots indicating reverse polarities in the spot group.

Illus.: Mt. Wilson and Mt. Palomar Observatories

Sunspots permit the rotational period of the sun to be deduced. Although spots are confined to intermediate solar latitudes, it is still possible to obtain a rotational period for the various parts of the sun, including the equatorial and polar regions, by using spectrographs. They do not come closer than five degrees to the equator and rarely do they extend to latitudes higher than 45°. By measuring the time it takes the spots to make a circuit of the sun, astronomers find that spots near the center of the sun have a period of about 24.6 days. At the latitude corresponding to New York, the rotational period is 27.5 days and at the poles the period is about 34 days. Thus an equatorial acceleration is evident in the motion of these spots. It also indicates that the sun cannot be a solid body. Were it a solid body, the internal forces acting on it would tear it apart. The sun must therefore be a gas.

The positions of the spots are dependent on the age of the current sunspot cycle. Early in the cycle the average solar latitude of the spots or active regions is between 30° and 35°. Several years later the latitude drops lower and lower until, at the end of the cycle, the spots are only five degrees from the equator.

Another characteristic of the sun that indicates its gaseous character is its surface temperature. Since we can measure the amount of energy we receive on the earth—93,000,000 miles away—we can use the inverse square law to determine the energy present on the sun and its surface temperature. By computing backwards, we can determine the amount of energy radiated from each square centimeter of the sun's surface. From this, the temperature can be derived. There are several ways in which this can be done, but the values given by the various methods do not differ too much. The temperature of the sun is about 10,800 degrees Fahrenheit. Nothing that we know of on the earth can exist as anything but a gas at this temperature. Thus, the sun is gaseous.

What is still more important is that as we penetrate deeper into the interior of the sun temperatures increase. Astronomers cannot physically penetrate the surface of the sun, but analytical boring tools have been fashioned which can yield a fairly definitive picture of its subsurface layers. As a result of these studies, astronomers believe the temperature of the sun increases to a center temperature of about 40,000,000 degrees Fahrenheit. A temperature of this magnitude ceases to have physical meaning but must be considered simply as a mathematical symbol which astronomers and physicists use to express the state of affairs at that point. Bertrand Russell once said, "It is the privilege of the pure mathematician not to know what he is talking about." When we speak of temperatures of this magnitude, his remark can be appreciated.

There exists a good reason for the temperature of the sun being what was indicated above. It is only at these tremendously high temperatures that the thermonuclear fires necessary to supply the sun with radiative energy can be maintained. The source of the sun's energy has been a source of speculation for many years. In years gone by it was believed that the sun was made of carbon, that is, coal. When scientists began learning more about the vast amount of energy coming from the sun, they soon realized that even if the entire sun were made of coal it could not last for more than 1500 years. Since the time scale was known to be considerably longer, it was obvious that the sun could not have been made of coal.

Some astronomers saw meteors flashing across the night sky. They speculated that perhaps these meteors were falling into the sun, burning up, to account for the energy being emitted. However, when more was learned about the concentration of these tiny bits of cosmic dust, it was realized that the supply was utterly insignificant. Thus meteors could not furnish the necessary energy.

The brilliant scientist, H. L. F. von Helmholtz, proposed that the slow contraction of the sun was converting the potential energy of the upper layers to radiative energy by which the sun shone. Again it was possible to deduce an age and scientists found that this process could not go on for more than 15,000,000 years without the sun exhausting its energy supply. As geologists insisted that the earth was perhaps several billion years old, this theory went by the boards.

A significant event took place in 1896 when radioactivity was discovered by Henri Becquerel. For the first time scientists discovered that the atom was not the smallest particle in nature. Atoms could disintegrate spontaneously and, with this break-up, energy was emitted. Shortly thereafter radium was isolated by Pierre and Maria Curie and instantly scientists seized upon this substance as the source of solar energy. Unfortunately, even if the sun were made wholly of radium—which they knew it was not— the necessary energy would not be available. Thus, at the turn of the century, no tenable theory existed to explain the creation of the energy coming from the sun. Its source was a mystery.

With the discovery of the neutron in 1933 and its use in atom-smashing experiments, scientists learned that certain atomic reactions were possible. Then protons or hydrogen nuclei were also used for atom smashing, and during the mid-1930's a fantastic volume of research was performed in the laboratories in which not only neutrons but electrons and protons were used as "bullets." Scientists found that by using protons they could transmute carbon to nitrogen. They could change nitrogen to oxygen. Some of the elements created were radioactive and spontaneously broke down to yield a different element. This then was the situation in the late 1930's.

Dr. Hans Bethe, returning by train from a meeting of theoretical physicists in Washington, thought about these reactions and, on the back of an envelope, figured out a sequence by which protons are combined to form helium using the carbon atom as a catalyst. All the reactions necessary to perform this transmutation had been performed in the laboratory. When he had finished his task, he had set down the details of a six-stage process by which hydrogen is consumed in the sun to generate its energy with helium as the end product. Curiously, this solar phoenix theory was discovered independently by Dr. Carl von Weiszacker in Germany.

In the carbon cycle Dr. Bethe showed how four hydrogen nuclei could be absorbed in a process whereby the carbon acts as a catalyst and the end result is a helium atom. The carbon atom is left to

enter again into the reaction. At three stages of the six-stage process, energy is liberated. As four hydrogen nuclei weigh about 0.7%
more than the helium atom, it is this 0.7% of the mass that puts
in an appearance as energy.

Another process by which hydrogen can be transmuted into
helium with a release of energy is the proton-proton reaction. This
is a much simpler process than the carbon cycle since only hydrogen is involved in the reactions. In this process there is a union of
two protons to create an atom of heavy hydrogen or deuterium. It
is possible for another proton to unite with a deuteron to create the
light isotope of helium called tralphium. This isotope has two protons and one neutron. If two atoms of tralphium unite, the product
will be an atom of helium of mass four and two protons which
again participate in nuclear reactions. The difference in weight
between the four protons and the helium atom is the mass which
disappears as energy.

Which of these processes is present in the sun? The answer is
that these reactions are extremely sensitive to the core temperatures
of the stars. If the temperature is very high, then in all probability
the carbon cycle is dominant and accounts for the generation of
energy within the star. At lower temperatures the proton-proton
reaction is dominant. Astronomers now believe that in our sun the
temperature is too low for the carbon cycle and the proton-proton
reaction is responsible for energy generation.

In either reaction 564,000,000 tons of hydrogen are converted
to 560,000,000 tons of helium every second. The difference in the
two weights, 4,000,000 tons, is the amount of matter transformed
into energy every second and radiated away by the sun. At the
earth's distance from the sun we receive only a two-billionth of the
energy radiated by the sun. However, this two-billionth means that
four pounds of radiation are falling to the earth every second!
Thus the earth is gaining weight at the rate of four pounds per
second.

At this rate, how long will the sun last? Previously we discovered
that the sun was about one-third of a million times as massive

as the earth. This is a tremendous amount of matter, for it represents about two thousand million billion billion tons. If we radiate away 4,000,000 tons a second it means that in a year we will radiate away 120 million million tons of matter as energy and consume about 140 times as much hydrogen to do it. Under these circumstances it might appear that the sun should be a short-lived body. Yet a bit of simple arithmetic indicates that our sun, if made of only one-third hydrogen, will last for 40 billion years! Indeed we do not have to worry about our sun going out or burning itself out. How long has it been shining? For this we go to the rocks wherein lie buried records of the past. There are fossils in rocks which indicate that for the past few billion years the sun has been shining at approximately the same rate. Thus our sun appears to be quite young. Perhaps ten per cent of its lifetime is over. We still have a long way to go.

With the advent of space travel and the beginning of manned trips into space, our sun assumes an added significance, for not only is it the source of a benign energy which permits life to continue on the earth, but it is also the source of a fearful supply of lethal radiation which can doom a man as he travels through the unfriendly and alien environment of space.

From the sun comes the entire range of radiation in the electromagnetic spectrum. At one end of the scale we find the most energetic particles—cosmic rays. As we move to longer wavelengths we find gamma rays, X-rays, ultraviolet radiation and finally visible light. Toward the red end we find infrared, heat waves, radio waves and then electric waves. The sun is the source of all these radiations.

However, we live at the bottom of an atmosphere which absorbs most of this radiation. Life as we know it has evolved beneath this protective atmosphere because when the diluted radiations reach the surface they cease to be lethal. We are pierced by cosmic rays on the earth's surface, but these are secondary cosmic rays and contain about one-millionth of the energy of the primary cosmic rays found 25 miles up. Most of the other radiations are absorbed

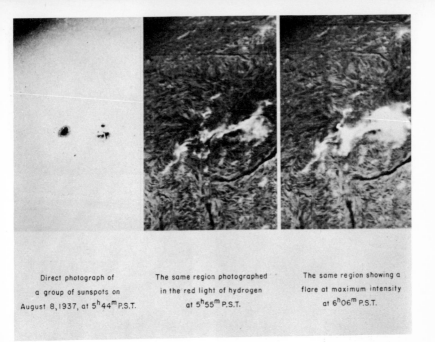

Direct photograph of a group of sunspots on August 8, 1937, at 5^h44^m P.S.T.

The same region photographed in the red light of hydrogen at 5^h55^m P.S.T.

The same region showing a flare at maximum intensity at 6^h06^m P.S.T.

Fig. 8-8 The development of a solar flare.

Illus.: Mt. Wilson and Mt. Palomar Observatories

so that only a tiny amount gets through. What gets through does not harm us. However, when man goes into space the full impact of solar radiations will be experienced.

Although a shielded or "storm cellar" cell in a space ship can protect astronauts from all radiations except cosmic rays—they will have to learn to live with these—there are times when the sun acts up and an abrupt storm on it will be manifest as a solar flare. When this occurs solar radiation can increase by a factor of 100,-000. The flare rise in brightness is almost explosive, taking place in from one to ten minutes. Depending on the brightness, very large flares may last longer than two hours. Thus the rise is steep and the decay quite slow.

Solar flares, on occasion, can eject irregular, fast-moving clouds of charged particles. The arrival of these particles and the radiation react with the earth to give rise to magnetic storms, auroral displays, disruption of the earth's magnetic field, disturbance of shortwave radio communications and other subtle changes.

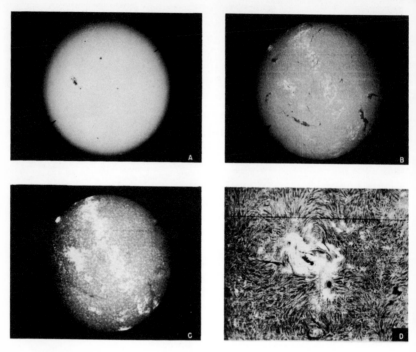

Fig. 8-9   Four views of the sun with the development of a solar flare.
(a) The sun in white light.
(b) The sun in hydrogen light.
(c) The sun in calcium light.
(d) A close-up of the flare in hydrogen light.

Illus.: Mt. Wilson and Mt. Palomar Observatories

One form that this radiation takes is the cosmic ray which, in this case, is high-energy protons. In the flare which occurred on July 7, 1959, it was estimated that the total radiation dosage may have reached 200 rem,* even with a radiation shielding of eight grams per square centimeter. The permissible, one-in-a-lifetime, dosage for workers in a radiation environment is set by the Atomic Energy Commission at 25 rem.

Fortunately, scientists seem to have found a correlation between the penumbra of a sunspot and the occurrence of solar flare. They

---

* A rem (<u>R</u>oentgen <u>E</u>quivalent <u>M</u>an) is a unit of radiation that results in the same biological damage as one roentgen of short wavelength electromagnetic radiation.

find that flares occur in complex sunspot groups which have a life-time in excess of one week. Actually, the area of the penumbra is used as an index for these predictions.

It has been discovered that predictions could be made to permit four-day trips into space. Scientists look for short-lived spots. When these are present and the size of the penumbra does not exceed a certain criterion, the odds are in favor of a four-day period in which flares will not occur. Thus, under these conditions, a four-day trip can be undertaken which is long enough for an expedition to reach the moon.

Until such time as very heavy shields can be put into space to absorb these lethal radiations, solar flares present a threat to all space travelers.

CHAPTER 9

The Stars

THOSE WHO SELDOM look at a starry sky see little more than the brightest objects. With a little time and a dark moonless sky, many hundreds of stars of assorted brightnesses and colors can be seen. Ancient observers had a richer opportunity to enjoy the heavens because they lived at the time of little night light. Bright artificial lights were still millenia away. Today, because of the dust, smoke and glare of lights, we rarely see all of the several thousand stars visible to the naked eye. The few we do see are for the most part clustered in groups and patterns. The ancients divided the sky into areas containing these groups or patterns of stars, and these groups have been preserved to this present day.

BRIGHTNESSES OF STARS

More than 20 centuries ago the Greek astronomer Hipparchus classified the stars according to their brightness into what we call *magnitudes.* The 20 brightest stars he chose to call first-magnitude stars; a few score others, less bright, were those of the second magnitude; still fainter ones were of the third and finally the great host of those just barely visible to the unaided eye were of the sixth magnitude.

We have preserved, extended and refined this arbitrary scheme of Hipparchus. About a century ago it was decided that the average star of first magnitude is 100 times brighter than a star of sixth magnitude. Using the average of the original 20 stars of Hipparchus means that some of those 20 are now considered to be brighter than the first magnitude. Thus there are stars of zero magnitude and the brightest star in the sky, Sirius, has a magnitude of −1.6, more than ten times as bright as the star considered to be exactly of first magnitude. The ratio of brightness between two successive magnitudes is 2.512, so a star of magnitude 1.0 is 2.512 times brighter than one of magnitude 2.0, which in turn is 2.512 times brighter than one of magnitude 3.0, and so on. The faintest star Hipparchus could see was of magnitude 6, but the advent of the telescope made it necessary for us to go to fainter magnitudes (larger numbers).

The magnitude of the sun is −26.8, which is 25 magnitudes brighter than Sirius. With a factor of 100 times for each five magnitudes, this works out to $100 \times 100 \times 100 \times 100 \times 100$, or 10,000,000,000 times. The stellar magnitude of the average full moon is −12.5; the sun, then, is about 14 magnitudes brighter than the moon, or about 400,000 times as bright. The planet Venus has a maximum magnitude of −4.4; it is then 15 times as bright as Sirius. The planet Uranus at best is of magnitude 5.7, barely visible to the unaided eye. A good pair of binoculars reveals stars of magnitude 10.5. Through the 200-inch telescope, theoretically, stars almost of magnitude 21 should be visible. With larger telescopes, however, there are considerations other than mere increase of aperture over smaller instruments. Through any telescope, stars fainter than those visible to the unaided eye can be photographed. With the 200-inch, stars of magnitude 23 can be photographed, but are not visible to the eye directly through the telescope.

With the sun's apparent magnitude at about −27 and the faintest photographable star at about 23, we have today a range of 50 magnitudes, or a factor of 100 billion billion times (100,000,000-000,000,000,000). This represents an enormous range in apparent brightnesses, but it cannot be a true measure of the range in intrinsic brightnesses because objects in the universe are not at the same distances from us. If it were possible to determine the distances of the stars, we could somehow discover their intrinsic, or absolute magnitudes.

THE DISTANCES TO THE STARS

It is easy to perform a simple experiment demonstrating the phenomenon called parallax. Hold up your index finger about ten inches before your face. Close one eye and note where the finger appears to stand against the background when viewed with the eye that was closed for the first observation. This shifting of apparent position or direction of an object when viewed from two places (the two eyes) is called *parallax, or parallactic shift.*

Let's extend this experiment another step. Hold the finger at arm's length and repeat the sighting with first one eye and then the other. The parallactic shift now is not so great. Repeat again, this time with the finger held up practically at the tip of the nose. The shift is much greater. In other words, the amount of the parallactic shift can be used to measure the distance to the object.

In a similar fashion we can measure the distances to the stars. Our "eyes" are many millions of miles apart, however, as we view a star first from one point of the earth's orbit and, months later, from another point of the orbit. A distant star will appear to change its position only slightly, perhaps too little to permit measurement of its shift. A closer star will appear to shift by a measurable amount, when we compare its place with respect to the distant stars on one photograph, taken at one time of year, and another similar photograph taken months later.

Because we may make many photographs of a certain star field at many different times, we can obtain several values of the parallax of a nearby star in that field, and their agreement or departure from agreement provides us with a measure of the reliability of the value we finally adopt. Our tabulated parallaxes are based upon the supposition that we have observed the star from the sun and also from an end of the radius of the earth's orbit. Our two "eyes," then, are 93,000,000 miles apart. It is a difficult and most precise problem, so much so that in the more than 100 years of application with large telescopes, only 6000 trigonometric parallaxes have been measured acceptably.

The nearest star visible to the unaided eye is Alpha Centauri, a star not above our horizon in mid-northern latitudes. Its parallax is 0.756 second of arc. This means that, at the distance of that star, the radius of the earth's orbit would subtend an angle of slightly more than three-quarters of a second of arc, and there are 1,296,-000 seconds of arc in a circle. Remember, this is the nearest of the stars. Parallaxes have been measured one-hundredth that of Alpha Centauri. To appreciate how small is the angle generated by this nearest star, suppose that you view a tiny point of light 11.3 miles distant, first with one eye, then the other. Its parallactic shift would be 0.756 second or, if you view a silver quarter two miles away, it will appear to be of the same size as the earth's orbit viewed from Alpha Centauri!

The parallax of 0.756 second corresponds to a distance of 25,-340,000,000,000 miles, and this is the nearest star! The mile is an awkward unit for use in expressing distances in the universe because the numbers become so large. In our solar system, as mentioned earlier, we use the the astronomical unit, the distance of the earth from the sun. Thus we may say that Jupiter's distance from the sun is 5.2 astronomical units, whereas that of Pluto is 39.5. The distance from the sun to Alpha Centauri is 273,000 astronomical units, a number still too large for comfort.

We seek a very long unit of distance, so our numbers can be whittled down. A picturesque one is the light-year, the distance that light can traverse in one year, traveling at a speed of 186,300 miles per second. The length of the light-year is, as we discovered in Chapter 2, 5,880,000,000,000 miles and, when we divide this into the distance of Alpha Centauri, we can say that the distance to that star is 4.31 light-years, a much more comfortable number to handle.

One of the nearest stars visible to us in mid-northern latitudes is the brightest of them all, Sirius, whose distance is 8.7 light years. We have seen that the sun appears to be 10,000,000,000 times as bright as this star, but we know that the sun is much nearer than Sirius. How would the two compare if we were to set them side by side? In fact, why not set at the same distance all the stars whose distances have been measured, so that we can compare their absolute magnitudes, instead of their apparent magnitudes?

Here another unit of distance comes into play. It bears a coined name—*parsec*—and it is the distance such that the radius of the earth's orbit subtends exactly one second of arc; in other words, a star with a parallax of one second would be at a distance of one parsec. No star (save the sun) is that close. With a parallax of 0.756 second, Alpha Centauri is 1.32 parsecs distant. A parsec is 206,265 astronomical units, or 3.259 light-years.

Astronomers have arbitrarily adopted the distance of ten parsecs as that at which we will put all stars in order to compare their intrinsic brightnesses. The apparent magnitude a star would have at that distance is what we shall call the absolute magnitude of the star.

The sun dims by more than 31 magnitudes when we push it out to a distance of ten parsecs; its absolute magnitude is close to 5.0. Sirius, actually at 2.67 parsecs, dims by 2.87 magnitudes at a distance of ten parsecs and becomes of absolute magnitude 1.3. This is more than 3.5 magnitudes brighter than the sun; intrinsically, Sirius is about 25 times brighter than our sun.

Of the 50-odd stars within five parsecs of the sun, only three are intrinsically brighter than the sun, not one of them a real record-setter. We know of stars with absolute magnitude −7, and, in general, those of absolute magnitude zero and brighter are thought of as "giants." One star in our neighborhood has absolute magnitude 16.6; but the record for faintness is held by a star about 6 parsecs distant, its absolute magnitude is 19.3. From the brightest known star to the faintest there is a range of about 26 magnitudes and the sun is about midway between the extremes. Today we consider the sun as an average star, as far as luminosity is concerned, and as one of the most numerous class of stars formerly called "dwarfs" but now designated as "main sequence" stars.

PHYSICS OF THE STARS

What else can we learn about stars? In terrestrial laboratories, we can use all of our senses to test and understand materials; we can handle matter in its various forms. We can put it into unusual environments to see how it behaves. In our study of the stars, we are confined to the use of only one of our senses—that of sight. We can receive only radiations from the stars, and in those signals we must read messages concerning all that we wish to know about them.

For example, we see that stars are of different colors. These are criteria of temperature, but we did not know that until we had obtained the spectra of the stars. When white light is passed through a prism, it is broken up and spread out into its component wavelengths. The short wavelengths produce the sensation of violet in our eye-mind mechanism; wavelengths about twice as long produce the sensation of red. Between these extremes lie the wavelengths of blue, green, yellow and orange. Beyond the violet lies the ultraviolet; beyond the red is the infrared. The ultraviolet can be detected easily by photographic plates, the infrared by thermocouples or other heat-receiving devices, although both regions can be detected in some measure or other by either of these detection devices.

In the laboratory, we have determined the laws underlying the analysis of these spectra. An incandescent solid or liquid, or a gas under high pressure, emits light that produces a *continuous spectrum*, an uninterrupted rainbow-colored band of light from infrared through the visible into the ultraviolet. A glowing gas under conditions of low pressure emits what scientists call a bright line or *emission spectrum*. This spectrum consists of only discrete, colored lines with dark spaces between them. If a gas under low pressure is placed in front of a source of a continuous spectrum, the continuous spectrum will be seen, but missing from it will be the same lines that the gas alone would give. In other words, a gas at low pressure absorbs from a continuous spectrum the same wave lengths it would emit were it excited by radiation so that it glowed. We call this an *absorption spectrum*.

Suppose we permit the light of the sun to pass through a spectroscope, that is, an optical instrument built around a prism, to break up the light into its component colors. The most modern instruments replace the prism with a diffraction grating, a polished plate of metal ruled with thousands of grooves per inch. The grating serves the same purpose as a prism in forming a spectrum. The sun's spectrum has a continuous background because of the light emanating from the denser interior gases. Absorption lines cross it in great profusion, because the mixture of scores of vaporized chemical elements in the thin surface layers is at low pressure. Each chemical element's atoms absorb only certain wavelengths, whether in the laboratory or in the sun, so we can untangle the maze of absorption lines in the solar spectrum and discover that about 75% of the known chemical elements are present in the sun.

Thus we can analyze the chemical composition of the atmosphere of any star bright enough to permit its spectrum to be photographed. We find that some of them disclose predominantly the lines of the lighter chemical elements; these are the bluish and white stars. Other stars have the lighter elements in them but in addition there are the lines arising from the intermediate elements such as the metals. These are the yellowish stars like the sun. Still other stars, orange or reddish, have all these lines and, in addition, lines due to molecules.

In this last type of spectrum we find the clue to the meaning of this sequence of spectral types. Only under conditions of relatively low temperature can molecules, particularly molecules of heavy metallic elements, exist. If a molecule is subjected to a sufficiently high temperature, it must dissociate into its component atoms. If the temperature is raised still higher, even some of the electrons of the atoms will be driven off, and so we find the lines due to the ionized atoms in the hot white stars.

TEMPERATURES OF THE STARS

The continuous backgrounds of stellar spectra also differ. Some of them have their strongest portions in the deep violet, others in the blue and green, still others farther toward the red. In the laboratory we can experiment to determine what this means, and again we find that it is an effect of temperature. The white stars look white because the strongest portions of their continuous spectra are in the short wavelength region; the red stars are that color because the regions of maximum intensity are in the longer wavelength range. By a combination of observational and theoretical techniques, we can actually evaluate the temperatures of the stars from their spectra.

The white and blue-white stars range in temperature up to 20,000 and 30,000 degrees Fahrenheit at their surfaces. The yellow stars, like the sun, have temperatures of 10,000 degrees or more. The reddish stars have temperatures of about 5000 or 6000 degrees Fahrenheit. The ranges are given here for general classes of stars; individual spectra can, of course, lead to individual determinations of temperature.

STELLAR DIAMETERS

Now we are prepared to perform what at the moment must seem to be at least a minor miracle. We shall determine the diameters of the stars, despite the fact that no star except the sun is close enough to us to permit us to see it as anything but a tiny point, even in the greatest telescopes. In fact, the larger the telescope the smaller the point of light, because of certain optical principles involved.

Again we go to the laboratory and, from many experiments and carefully contrived theory, we find that the amount of energy radiated by a luminous body depends on the fourth power of the temperature. That is, if we have one star with the same temperature as another, we can be sure that each square inch of each star radiates the same amount of energy. If one of the stars is brighter than the other—that is, on the absolute magnitude basis—it must be because it has more square inches of surface. For example, the star Sirius, instead of being a single star it is the principal star of a physical pair. Its companion is 8.7 magnitudes fainter—about 1/3000th as bright—yet the two stars are of almost identical temperature. The difference must be a matter of size and, when we perform the necessary mathematics, we discover that the diameter of Sirius must be more than 50 times as great as that of its faint companion.

However, remember that the rule is that emission of energy per unit area of surface varies as the fourth power of the temperature; that is, $T \times T \times T \times T$. The temperature of Sirius is 1.75 that of our sun, so we multiply $1.75 \times 1.75 \times 1.75 \times 1.75$ and find that each square inch of Sirius radiates 9.38 times as much energy as the same area of the sun. Area for area, Sirius radiates almost ten times as much energy as the sun. We have already seen that Sirius is about 25 times as bright as the sun intrinsically, and now we have found that 9.8 times is due to temperature, so a factor of 2.67 must represent the amount due to size, actually area. The diameter of Sirius, then, must be 1.63 times that of our sun, or about 1,400,000 miles; the faint companion's diameter is only 25,600 miles, only a trifle smaller than Neptune.

In this way, when we have determined the absolute magnitude through knowing the star's distance, and the temperature from its spectrum, we can calculate its diameter, even though, through the greatest telescope, it appears to be only a point.

We may recall that astronomers thought of the stars of bright absolute magnitude as giants in luminosity, and faint stars as dwarfs. When we have calculated their diameters, we find that these terms—giant and dwarf—also apply to physical size. For the ordinary white and bluish stars, there is a comparatively small range of diameter; for the red stars, there is a great range, perhaps as much as 20,000 times or more. There are some unusual white stars of small size, known as white dwarfs—the companion of Sirius is an example—but these are not nearly as common as the red dwarfs. From a few thousand miles in diameter for these white dwarfs, we jump to the red giants with diameters in some instances of 200 or more times the diameter of our sun, large enough to include the orbit of Mars if they were centered at the sun. One is suspected to be so large that it would include the orbit of Saturn if it were centered at the sun, whereas still others are believed to be so huge and tenuous that their materials may thin out into space without any definite boundary.

STELLAR MASSES

How many more miracles of detection can we work? Can we hope to determine the masses of the stars? We can! There exist pairs of stars revolving around their common center of gravity— binary stars whose motions can be observed and plotted until we know their orbits with great accuracy. Here we fall back on the law of gravitation, which tells us that the greater the attraction between two bodies, the greater the product of their masses. At the same distance apart, two heavy masses will then revolve around their common center more rapidly than two light masses; otherwise the greater attraction would pull them together. The centrifugal force of the orbital motion must balance the gravitational attraction between the two bodies.

The best way to approach this is to use a specific example. The earth revolves around the sun in an equilibrium orbit because it has a certain mass and is at a certain distance from the sun. Suppose that, instead of a body with a mass equal to the earth, there was substituted a body of mass equal to the sun, 333,000 times as heavy as the earth. In order to counteract a too great gravitational attraction, this body and the sun would need to revolve in a period of 258.26 days, instead of the present 365.25 days of the year. Suppose the mass of the sun were doubled; again the period would be only 258.26 days for a body of the earth's mass. In other words, it is the total mass of the pair of bodies that governs the period of revolution in an orbit of any given size. If we find a pair of stars separated by the same distance as the earth and the sun, and the period is 365¼ days, the total mass of the system will be equal to the sun's mass (plus the tiny extra mass of the earth); if the period is only 258.26 days, the total mass is twice that of the sun. Of course, we can calculate the total mass for the system from any observed period for any observed separation of the two stars.

We must know the distance of the binary system in order to determine the linear distance between the two stars, in miles, from the observed angular separation. Sometimes the binary is too distant for parallax measurement; if so, we bring into play a method of determination called the *spectroscopic* parallax. We have seen that the cool red stars are known to have certain absolute magnitudes, on the average, as do stars of all other spectrum types. As soon as we have studied the spectrum of a star, we can determine its absolute magnitude and this, compared with its apparent magnitude, will disclose the distance. Even if we can determine only the color of a star, we can make a good guess at its distance, because color is an index of absolute magnitude.

So far, of course, we have determined only the total mass of the system and not the masses of the individual stars of the pair. This refinement is possible only if we can determine the relative sizes of the two orbits around the common center of gravity of the pair. If the orbit of one is twice as great as that of the other, the first star is only half as massive as the second one. If we then know the total mass of the system in terms of the sun's mass and have determined the ratio of masses, we can calculate the individual masses in terms of the sun. When we have done so for a great many stars, we find that for most stars there is a very definite relationship between mass and luminosity, but masses range through a much smaller set of values than that for luminosities. The star of smallest known mass is 0.008 times as heavy as the sun; the heaviest stars are scarcely 100 times as massive as the sun.

There are some stars that, although small, are quite massive; they conform to the mass-luminosity relationship, because they are very dense. The average material of the companion of Sirius weighs many tons per pint! Such stars are known as white dwarfs, from the first few that were discovered; today we believe that there exist these unusual stars in all colors permitted to normal stars. At the other extreme, there are the great, bloated, cool red giants whose average densities are scarcely greater than that of the matter in a man-made vacuum.

There are stars known that appear to be traversing slightly waving paths through the sky and these, we know, are accompanied by as yet undiscovered companions. In one instance, we can determine the mass of the unseen companion as only $\frac{1}{60}$th than that of the bright star. In this and in some other cases we may be discovering without seeing objects of roughly planetary dimensions. If there can be companions of such low mass, there may be companions of much lower mass, as well, revolving around other stars but not disturbing them sufficiently to permit our detection of their wavy motions. In this kind of observation we find considerable assurance that many stars may be accompanied by systems of planets, and life may exist in many parts of the universe.

VARIABLE STARS

Variable stars—stars of changing brightness—are observed, and some of them, we know, are binary systems whose orbits are turned edge-on toward us. Periodically the two stars eclipse each other as they revolve around their common center of gravity. Other variables, however, change their intrinsic brightnesses, either by swelling up and contracting more or less rhythmically or because of some form of spottedness like that of our sun, which itself is a slightly variable star.

The red variables for the most part have long periods, of the order of a few months or years. The white and yellowish stars have shorter periods and some of these, with periods ranging from a few hours to about three months, go through their variations in very regular periods, precise to the second as nearly as we can tell. We have discovered that there is a definite relationship between the periods of these *cepheid* variables, as they are called, and their luminosities. The longer the period the brighter is the cepheid. One with a two-day period is 600 times brighter than the sun whereas one with a period of 50 days is 15,000 times brighter than the sun. Although there are a few cepheids with different metal compositions in their outer atmosphere which do not conform precisely to the period-luminosity relationship, astronomers of Mt. Palomar have resolved the difficulties so that their use as a celestial yardstick is maintained.

The 610 cepheids in our Milky Way are easy to recognize from their regular periods and manner of variation and provide us with one of our most powerful tools for determining great distances. As soon as we have measured the period, we know the absolute magnitude; when we compare this with the apparent magnitude, we can calculate the distance to the star. Because the cepheid scale can be used quite accurately to a distance of five million light-years, they can be used to determine the distances to the nearest galaxies.

NOVAE AND SUPERNOVAE

Some variable stars are cataclysmic in their behavior, in a few hours or days increasing their energy output by thousands for the ordinary novae or even millions for the prodigious supernovae. This is ten trillion trillion times the energy released by a hydrogen bomb. In many instances novae have been photographed years before they have called themselves to our attention by blowing up. After a brief time, hours, days, weeks or even years, the nova fades, usually into the same obscurity from which it came. On a later occasion, perhaps after many years, the nova may go through the performance again, and in no instance do we have evidence that the nova totally destroys itself. Actually only a small portion of the star, probably a portion of its surface layers, is blown off. However, in the case of the supernovae, some astronomers believe that the stars blow up and completely destroy themselves.

We can measure the motion of the expanding gas layers with the spectroscope. Just as the pitch of a sound changes if the distance between us and its source is changed, so the "pitch" of light waves changes with a change of distance of the source. If the distance is increasing, the spectrum lines are shifted toward the red; a decreasing distance produces a shift toward the violet. The amount of the shift is a measure of the rate of changing distance. Radical velocities obtained from novae explosions show that material rushes outward from the star at great speeds and often, years later, we find a nebulous mass of material surrounding such a star, as visible proof that some of the star's substance was blown off.

Proceeding from our perception here on earth of a feeble pulse of light from a star, we have devised instruments and methods for determining distances, temperatures, diameters, masses, chemical compositions and motions. Surely, if we tend sometimes to think of man as being rather insignificant in view of the great dimensions of the cosmos, we must reconsider and insist that the probing, keen mind of man is the most marvelous phenomenon yet discovered in all the universe.

CHAPTER 10

The Milky Way
and Beyond

THE LATE Dr. Edwin P. Hubble once said, "The history of astronomy is a history of receding horizons." So it has been. In ancient days our ancestors raised their eyes to the skies from atop high hills to see only the sun, the moon, a few thousand stars and five star-like objects that changed their places with respect to each other and against the background of the stars. These they called the "wandering stars" or planets. There were the "falling stars" or meteors that appeared frequently as streaking points of light sometimes leaving behind them for a brief time a glistening train. Occasionally there appeared a "hairy star" or comet, a ghostly tailed object lingering for a few days or weeks, moving slowly among the stars and waxing and waning in brightness, at last either fading into invisibility or slipping out of sight into the twilight.

EARLY IDEAS OF THE UNIVERSE

Restricted to a relatively small part of the world, ancient civilizations readily built up a picture of the universe as a flat or slightly dome-shaped earth above which the sun and other heavenly bodies, mysteriously suspended, were transported from east to west each day. The universe need be only a small one; the earth dominated it and man dominated the earth. It was an anthropocentric universe.

More than 20 centuries ago, in Greece, philosophers developed the novel but really simpler theory that the earth, a ball, rotates on its axis each 24 hours, turning eastward beneath the objects in the sky to make them appear to roll westward over us. More than two centuries before the Christian era the size of the earth was measured and even more advanced notions had been developed: that the earth revolves around the sun as one of the planets and that the stars are extremely distant, not mere specks of fire attached to a relatively small crystalline sphere centered on the earth.

There arose astronomers who, not content with merely speculating about what might be, made measurements of what they saw, recording for us the changing positions of the planets so that others following them might derive fundamental laws about the behavior of bodies in space. At last, more than three centuries ago, came the invention of the telescope and its application to astronomy.

Instantly, enormously more than the human eye alone had seen or the human mind had conceived was revealed. Soon all agreed that the earth was not the center of the universe, even the sun was not, and today we know that our own great system of stars is not the center. Not only stars in enormous numbers, in pairs and clusters and clumps, but blobs and wisps of misty light called nebulae, were discovered and catalogued. Strange vacancies, as though space had been swept clean, were seen here and there; new planets and satellites were discovered.

Today our largest telescopes explore realms of space where distance and dimension have surrendered their meaning. Monstrous radio telescopes, picking up long wavelength radiations not discoverable in any other way, probe even beyond the limits of our optical telescopes. Yet we find that we can classify all the objects we detect into relatively few categories. More important to man's opinion of himself, we can understand most of what we see and we can speculate intelligently about what we do not immediately comprehend.

STRUCTURE OF THE MILKY WAY

In a clear, moonless sky, in a place far from city lights, you may be startled to see an irregular band of hazy light wending its way up the sky like a river of stars. This Milky Way is made up of the combined light of 100 billion stars. Irregular in width and contour, it is not as conspicuous in the winter sky as it is in summer. Low on the southern horizon in summertime, its breadth and brightness call attention to the region of the constellation of Sagittarius, the Archer, the direction of the center of our system of stars, an island in the universe. From Sagittarius, a curious, dark band

Fig. 10-1 The North American nebula found in the summer Milky Way in Cygnus.

Illus.: Mt. Wilson and Mt. Palomar Observatories

Fig. 10-2 The Milky Way as seen in the direction toward its center in Sagittarius.

Illus.: Mt. Wilson and Mt. Palomar Observatories

furrows up the Milky Way to Cygnus, the Swan, and splits it into two branches. Still other patches cut the two bands at right angles to give to it a mottled appearance.

The Milky Way system or galaxy is shaped somewhat like a pocket watch or, perhaps a little more exactly, like the athlete's discus. Its size is tremendous—100,000 light-years in diameter. At its center the thickness is about 15,000 light-years, tapering down to less than 10,000 light-years near the rim. Our sun's location is about three-fifths of the way from the center toward one edge; hence, about 30,000 light-years from the center.

To revert to our analogy of the pocket watch, we are located not in the median plane, but approximately at the hub of the second hand of the watch. When we look toward Sagittarius in the summer sky, we are looking from the second hand toward the center of the watch; when we look toward Perseus and Auriga in the winter sky, we are looking away from the center, toward the rim. If we extend the shaft of the second hand of the watch in both directions, one end points toward Coma Berenices, the other toward Sculptor, a constellation invisible in mid-northern latitudes.

Our system is spinning in its own plane, but not like a wheel, because it is not a solid object. Made up of about 100 billion stars, more thickly crowded near the center, the galaxy rotates somewhat as the solar system does, with those stars farthest from the

Fig. 10-3   A galaxy seen "edge-on." Probably similar to a view of our Milky Way seen from the same orientation.

Illus.: Mt. Wilson and Mt. Palomar Observatories

Fig. 10-4 M-51 plus a satellite galaxy seen "broadside-on." The Milky Way would also disclose this pinwheel pattern when viewed from the proper position in space.

Fig. 10-5 The great nebula in Orion.

center moving most slowly. Our sun and its neighbors move with a velocity of about 175 miles per second, yet so great is our distance from the center that more than 200,000,000 years are required for one circuit.

CONTENT OF THE MILKY WAY

On the average, the stars are separated by distances some 30,000,000 times their own diameters. However, the space between them is by no means empty. We find gases, clouds of dust and isolated atoms and solid particles scattered throughout space. Today astronomers believe that the total mass of our galaxy is the equivalent of 200 billion stars, one-half of it organized in the form of stars, the remainder in the unorganized state of nebulae and individual particles.

A fruitful place to begin investigation of the nebulae is in the winter constellation of Orion, the Hunter. Just below the eastern star of Orion's belt is a dangling streamer of bright nebulosity, silhouetted against which is the Horsehead, a dark nebula, hiding some of the bright nebulosity and many stars that lie beyond it. In the swordhilt that lies below Orion's belt, a fuzzy patch of light is revealed as a brillant, chaotic mass of gas, a bright nebula intensively studied by astronomers.

Although the Great Nebula in Orion appears to be rather solid,

Fig. 10-6 The Pleiades—An open or galactic cluster. Some of the dust surrounding the stars and reflecting their light can be seen.

Illus.: Flower-Cook Observatories

we might contrast its density with that of the air we breathe, which weighs about one ounce per cubic foot. One ounce of the material comprising the Orion Nebula would cover the whole surface of the earth to a depth of one foot!

The spectroscope tells us that nebulae consist mostly of hydrogen slightly contaminated by oxygen, nitrogen and a few other common elements. We understand the mechanisms by which nebular gases glow. The light emitted by massive, blue-white stars is rich in ultraviolet radiation. The atoms of the gases of a nebula nearby, or one involving these stars, absorb the ultraviolet radiation, digest it and re-emit it in the visible form. Other bright nebulae are not really glowing. The "silver braid" involving the stars of the Pleiades, a cluster northwest of Orion, is a cloud of particles merely reflecting the light of the stars imbedded in it and scattering it much as particles of a fog scatter the light of a street lamp.

The dark nebulae that we detect because they hide stars and bright nebulae lying beyond them, as well as the nebulae of the Pleiades type, probably consist mostly of particles larger than single atoms—material that we might call dust. This dust is most effective in obscuring the light of the stars, which means we know that the size of the dust grains must be on the order of $\frac{1}{50,000}$th of an inch. The particles are probably molecular combinations involving hydrogen with carbon, oxygen and nitrogen.* At the temperature of interstellar space they may exist as ice particles. In addition to these particles, others involving metals must also

* These are the four basic elements of life. Is this just a coincidence?

be present. This cosmic dust is not limited to our Milky Way system but is common to all galaxies. Photographs of near and distant galaxies, particularly those seen edge-on, reveal a band of this obscuring material in the central plane. From dynamical considerations, astronomers believe that the mass of dust in our Milky Way just equals the mass of the 100 billion stars in the system.

Some of these dark nebulae, with diameters on the order of three or four light-years, have assumed a justified importance. These tiny, black patches in the sky may be embryonic stars. As time goes on the particles of a globule are compacted by radiation pressure from surrounding stars, then later by mutual gravitational attraction. Finally the globule begins to glow and becomes a star, its energy maintained by atomic processes at its core, as mentioned earlier.

Some luminous nebulae are rather small and, in some instances, rather symmetrically shaped. In Lyra, in the summer sky, is the best known of the so-called ring, or annular, nebulae. This object is really a spherical shell, with a star at its center—a star of peculiar properties and certainly the origin of the ultraviolet radiation that excites the glowing gases of the nebula. About 400 of these "planetary" nebulae are known, their name having arisen from the fact that the early telescopic astronomers saw that they presented disks, instead of starlike appearances. They are among the most distant recognizable objects in our galaxy, the known

Fig. 10-7 Nebula in Monoceros. Here can be seen the tiny dark globules which may be embryonic stars.

Illus.: Mt. Wilson and Mt. Palomar Observatories

Fig. 10-8 A planetary nebula in the constellation of Ursa Major.

Illus.: Mt. Wilson and Mt. Palomar Observatories

ones lying at distances from 3000 to 30,000 light-years. The typical planetary nebula has a diameter of a million million miles, about 250 times the distance from Pluto to the sun. The gases in these nebulae are of much lower density than the best artificial vacuum on earth. A matchbox full of hydrogen, slightly contaminated with dust and air, then blown up to the size of a large mountain, would have a density about as low as that of the materials of a planetary nebula.

The origin of these objects is a matter of current speculation, although some astronomers are convinced that there is a close tie between planetaries and the extravagant variable stars known as supernovae novae. In 1054 A.D., observant Chinese astronomers recorded a brilliant new star in the constellation of Taurus, the Bull, northwest of Orion. Today, nine centuries later, with a telescope we observe a tortured, chaotic patch of light at the same spot, a nebula consisting almost entirely of hydrogen and expand-

Fig. 10-9 Two views of the crab nebula in Taurus. The picture on the right is taken in white light, the other in hydrogen light.

Illus.: Mt. Wilson and Mt. Palomar Observatories

ing at such a rate that, nine centuries ago, the material could all have been at one spot. The supernova literally blew its top, throwing off, in a violent explosion, perhaps ten per cent of its mass which, still expanding, forms the so-called Crab Nebula in Taurus. It may well be that all planetary nebulae originated in this fashion.

Star clusters can be placed into two broad categories. The galactic or "open" clusters, containing from 20 to 20,000 members, are found in and near the Milky Way. Numbering about 300, they lie within 10,000 light-years of the sun. It is estimated that from five to ten times as many are in other parts of the Milky Way that we cannot see. Most of them are relatively easily resolved into individual stars. Some accidental alignments of stars could be mistaken for clusters, but in a true cluster the stars are all about the same distance from us and they all move in the same direction. The two most prominent clusters visible to the naked eye are the Pleiades and Hyades.

The striking, compact, globular clusters are densely packed aggregations of 10,000 to 1,000,000 stars, magnificently blazing at their centers from the combined light of thousands of stars that can not be distinguished separately. The distribution of these clusters is very significant; only a few of them are not found in the half of the sky that has Sagittarius and Scorpio at its center. This region, it will be recalled, is the direction of the center of our galaxy. About 100 globular clusters are known, and 30% of them are found in an area measuring only four per cent of the sky. These known clusters, and perhaps another 100 not yet discovered, are

Fig. 10-10   **The globular cluster in Canes Venatici.**

Illus.: Mt. Wilson and Mt. Palomar Observatories

arranged in a spherical distribution centered on the center of the galaxy. Astronomers have discovered that some 200 globular clusters are associated with the great Andromeda galaxy. From the detection of these clusters in the nearer galaxies, it is certain that almost all of the galaxies contain them.

Variable stars of many kinds are found, from the only slightly variable to the explosive such as the novae mentioned earlier. The very useful cepheid-type provides us with the means for measuring great distances. Ranging in period from 80 minutes for the shortest to about 100 days for the longest, these stars have luminosities that are correlated with their periods.

The short-period cepheids are found in globular clusters in considerable numbers, and through them we have determined the distances of these objects. The long-period cepheids are useful in determining the distances to the other galaxies.

OTHER GALAXIES

The early users of telescopes could not distinguish between the true gaseous or dust nebulae and other objects which today are revealed by great telescopes as other galaxies of stars with the same average dimensions and the same constitution, essentially, as our Milky Way system. One of the nearest is the great galaxy in Andromeda, at a distance of about 1,500,000 light-years. It contains stars and star clusters, nebulae, both bright and dark, star clouds and variable stars of all kinds. We have used the variables,

Fig. 10-11 A field of variable stars in the Andromeda galaxy. Two of the variables are bracketed by lines.

Illus.: Mt. Wilson and Mt. Palomar Observatories

Fig. 10-12 The great galaxy in Andromeda. The two satellite galaxies can also be seen.

some of the brightest stars and the globular clusters, to derive several confirmatory values of the distance. Like the Milky Way with its satellites—the Magellanic Clouds—the Andromeda galaxy also is accompanied by two satellite galaxies.

The Andromeda galaxy, faintly visible to the unaided eye, is revealed by photography through great telescopes as a spiral structure. Only recently, with the use of giant radio telescopes, we have verified that our Milky Way system is also a spiral galaxy.

Our galaxy, the spiral in Andromeda and some 17 other galaxies of various types form a small, compact, local system. The space

Fig. 10-13 One end of the Andromeda galaxy resolved into stars.

JUNE 9, 1950   FEB. 7, 1951

NOVA IN MESSIER 101

Fig. 10-14   Nova in Messier 101. These stars permit distance determinations to 30 million light years.

outside our own system is what Dr. Harlow Shapley calls the "meta-
galaxy." As we probe farther and farther into space we find many
clusters of galaxies. Today the great 200-inch, Hale telescope atop
Palomar Mountain reveals galaxies six billion light-years distant
and, in that enormous volume of space, our best estimate is that
there are at least a billion galaxies within reach of our present telescopes.

The spectroscope has revealed something most important concerning the galaxies. All but a few of the nearest ones possess spectra in which the lines are shifted toward the red. (The ones which
do not show this shift are influenced by the sun's motion around
the galactic center.) The generally accepted explanation of this
phenomenon, using physical laws as we know them today, is that
the distance between the source and the earth is increasing. For
every six million light-years, the velocity of recession is greater by
almost 100 miles per second. The greatest red-shift measured so
far is interpreted as a velocity of recession of 90,000 miles per
second, for a galaxy whose distance, then, is of the order of six
billion light-years!

CHAPTER 11

Tools of the Astronomer

W HEN WE SPEAK of the tools of the astronomer, we are inclined to think of telescopes, spectroscopes, cameras and so forth. Yet the most complex, most ingenious and most versatile optical tools we possess are our eyes. As human beings we tend to take them so much for granted. Yet, when we ponder the physical characteristics and function of the eye, we begin to appreciate its position as truly one of the wonders of nature.

To understand the eye, we might compare it to a camera. A camera has a lens which brings an image to focus on a photographic plate. The eye also possesses a lens which focuses the image on the retina. In a camera, when you change from a distant scene to an object a few feet away, it is necessary to change the focus or the image will be fuzzy. The eye has a lens capable of changing its curvature to account for change in distance and always yields a sharp image. The camera has a manual- or photo-cell-controlled iris diaphragm to prevent under- or over-exposure of the film. The eye also possesses an iris, but this one automatically adjusts the amount of light entering the eye. If you wish to take a black and white picture with your camera, you use a certain type of film. If you wish to photograph in color, it is necessary to use color film. The eye has an enviable versatility in this respect for it can always see color when color is present or just shades of black and white when color is absent.

The ability of the retina to observe faint light depends on a substance called *visual purple*. During the day this substance is lacking and the retina is relatively insensitive. When we are in darkness for a considerable period of time, the visual purple reforms, making the retina extremely sensitive; objects become visible in the faintest light. It is estimated that the range in brightness between sunlight falling on a sheet of white paper and say, darkness in an operating planetarium, represents over ten billion times.

However, there are certain limitations of the eye which have influenced the auxiliary instruments used by the scientists. Since the retina is a finely divided surface in the sense that the ends of the rods and cones form this surface, the eye has a certain resolving power or ability to differentiate two objects at a distance. One way of testing the resolution of the naked eye is to look at Alcor and Mizar, the two stars in the "break" of the handle of the Big Dipper. These stars are about 12 minutes of arc apart and furnish a convenient visual test. If we use a telescope that magnifies the objects, the resulting image on the retina will be larger with a greater separation between the stars, and we see the distant stars better.

THE TELESCOPE

When glass was discovered and came into common use, it was inevitable that some one would fashion a piece of glass with a curve on one side that would instantly reveal itself as a magnifying glass. Following the use of these as magnifiers and the increased facility with which the craftsmen of that time were working in glass, both the positive—magnifying—lenses and the negative—minifying—lenses were made. Despite these advances, it remained for Hans Lippershey, in 1608, to successfully position two of these lenses to form the prototype of all refracting telescopes.

In the hands of Lippershey the telescope was a novelty, a toy.

In 1609 Galileo heard of Lippershey's device and, being a skilled worker of glass, constructed his own telescope which he turned on the sky. This first astronomical telescope revealed new worlds in space and eventually sparked the beginning of a continuing thought revolution.

Essentially, a telescope is nothing more or less than a giant eye. Our eye has a lens about one-quarter of an inch in diameter. Thus the first small telescope built by Galileo, with a one-inch objective, could funnel some 16 times as much light into the eye as was seen by the eye alone. What was also significant was that the telescope could penetrate farther into space and the larger the telescope objective the more distant the objects observed. Thus the most important function of the telescope turned out to be the enlargement of the volume of space man could study.

Essentially, telescopes magnify celestial objects. This magnification is not, like the light-gathering power, a function of the objective size. The magnification is a variable. By a suitable arrangement of lenses we can vary the magnification of the telescope. To find the magnification we must know the focal length of the objective and the focal length of the eyepiece. The ratio of the two, that is, the focal length of the objective in inches divided by the focal length of the eyepiece in inches, yields the magnification of the system. Thus, if we have an objective with a focal length of 300 inches and use a half-inch eyepiece with it, the magnification will be 600 times. Actually, there is a practical limit to magnification and that is about 50 diameters to the inch. Thus, for a 24-inch telescope, the maximum magnification will be 24 × 50 or 1200 times.

We spoke about the resolving power of the eye and indicated that it is limited because of the curious structure of the retina. Using a telescope we magnify the object and, thus, enlarge it so that the object covers a larger part of the retina. In the case of the telescope, the ability to differentiate stars which are close together is the resolving power. This can be set down in a formula which for two stars of the sixth magnitude reads:

TOOLS OF THE ASTRONOMER

$$\text{resolving power} = \frac{4.56 \text{ seconds of arc}}{a}$$

where a represents the aperture of the telescope in inches. Thus the 100-inch telescope has a resolving power of 0.0456 seconds of arc.

Refracting telescopes were the first ones to be used, but early scientists discovered that they had inherent faults. There was *chromatic aberration*, which means that all the colors do not come to a focus at the same point. Even by using two different glasses for elements in the objective, some aberration was still present. To avoid this color Sir Isaac Newton made a reflecting telescope in which a mirror acted as the collector of light. Reflecting telescopes do not have chromatic aberration. Refracting telescopes have two-element objectives and this means that four surfaces have to be figured, ground and precisely made. In the reflector only one surface need be figured. Although the refractor tends to be long because of the necessary long focal lengths, the reflector can be folded so that the telescope does not become inordinately

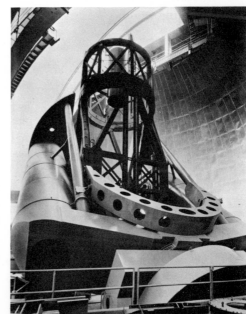

Fig. 11-1 200-inch Hale telescope on Mount Palomar pointing to Zenith as seen from the south.

Illus.: Mt. Wilson and Mt. Palomar Observatories

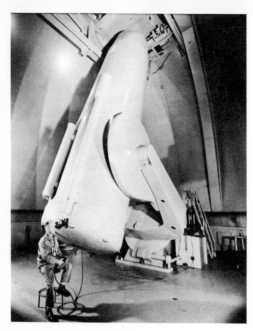

Fig. 11-2 60-inch Schmidt telescope on Mount Palomar. This telescope "bird dogs" for the 200-inch because of its ability to see "big." The 200-inch sees "deep."

Illus.: Mt. Wilson and Mt. Palomar Observatories

long. There were many reasons for the advances made in reflecting telescopes, and today the largest is of course of this type. The 100-ton, 200-inch, reflecting telescope at Mt. Palomar is the largest in the world.

THE SPECTROSCOPE AND FAMILY

The telescope marked the beginning of a line of tools and accessories astronomers developed to interpret what they see in the skies. One instrument fully as important as the telescope is the spectroscope. This is simply a glorified chandelier crystal whose sole function is to break up the light coming into the system into the component colors that make up the light.

Newton, in his classic experiments, showed that when white light is passed through a prism the light is bent or refracted and spread out into the colors of the rainbow. It is a peculiar property of a wedge of glass to bend violet light more than it bends red light. Thus it can break up white light into the spectrum. However, a simple prism does not make a spectroscope. A lens must be used to bring the light of the star to a focus. At this point the scientist places a slit. The diverging beam of light then falls on another lens which converts it into a parallel beam and this is what passes through the prism to be broken up. Once the light has passed through the prism, another lens is required to bring the light to a focus on some type of receiver.

In this way the astronomer can break up the light coming from a star, a nebula or the sun to interpret the physical condition and chemical compositon of the object.

Because the spectrum of, say, the sun contains dark lines—absorption lines—and only particular atoms of an element can steal the light at the place where the lines occur, it is possible to determine the chemical elements in the atmosphere of the sun from the spectrum. Likewise, the temperature of a star will determine the number and type of lines to be seen. Thus the very hot stars have relatively few lines, and they are lines of the light elements like hydrogen and helium. By the same token the spectra of certain cool stars show the presence of compounds, and, since we know at what temperature these compounds break up, we can ascertain the upper limit of temperature for these stars.

By seeing how far the lines in the spectrum of a star are shifted, it is possible to determine its radial velocity or speed directly away from or toward the earth. Even temperatures and sizes of stars can be derived by experts working with the spectra of stars.

It is not in the province of this book to detail these procedures, for they are quite involved and space precludes a full development of this technique. The important point is that with this type of auxiliary instrument the telescope not only reaches far into space but brings back some of the answers as to the physical state of matter in those remote places.

Operating on the same principle are other tools of astronomy which permit exploration of other bodies in the solar system.

Astronomers have constructed a spectrohelioscope that permits them to observe the sun in monochromatic light. To do this a spectroscope is used to break up the light of the sun into a spectrum, and the device then throws away all the light except for a dark line in the red due to hydrogen and an invisible wide, dark line complex in the blue due to calcium. These lines are used because they are the strongest in the spectrum. With this device the astronomer can observe the sun in either hydrogen light or photograph the sun in calcium light. Since eruptions on the sun involve these elements, we can see the infrequent solar storms or flares by observing the sun in this light. Except for one or two recorded instances, all flares of the sun are invisible in continuous light but are readily seen in hydrogen light. Recently a monochromator has been developed which uses quartz plates and polarizing screens to isolate the hydrogen line alone. Astronomers consider the monochromator a much more satisfactory instrument than the spectrohelioscope.

Within the past few years the photocell has assumed a most respected position in astronomy. Before World War II the photocell was a laboratory curiosity. Today these devices are highly developed and contribute significantly to many facets of astronomy. Originally they were used for measuring the variation in light coming from a star. Today, using color filters, astronomers are gaining an insight into the nature and content of space between the stars.

A startling innovation has been the marriage of the telescope to television. This is inherently a powerful combination of tools in which the potential is fantastically high. With the 200-inch telescope we can photograph an object with a magnitude of 23. The use of electronic amplification on telescopic images can increase the "reach" by one or two more magnitudes. Thus the net result of this new system is to provide a new reach for the telescope in probing space.

Another simple but highly useful device is the *coronagraph*. In this instrument the sun is artificially eclipsed, which permits the daily study of prominences and the inner corona of the sun. The trick in this device is that the lenses must be scrupulously clean, with no scratches or markings to produce any scattering of light in the telescope. Also, the location of the coronagraph is important; thus the successful ones are situated on high mountains, high above the dense, turbulent layers of the earth's atmosphere.

RADIO TELESCOPES

Until World War II optical telescopes were the only instruments used to probe the depths of space. However, after the war there became available a great many surplus radar dishes, and these sparked another revolution in astronomy—one which is to rank with the advances made by Galileo in his use of the telescope.

We are witnessing this revolution, and to understand its significance we must consider the content of space and its effect on our optical instruments.

Astronomers had known for a long time that there were scattered clouds of gas, dust and obscuring material in interstellar space. In addition to the bright clouds which glow because they are excited by starlight, there are dark, obscuring clouds which can be seen only because they blot out the light of stars behind them. The curious thing about this obscuring dust is that the particle size is almost of the same size as the wavelength of light in the visible region of the spectrum, that is, the wavelength of the radiation—about 1/50,000th of an inch. Thus, the light from a distant star is dimmed by the time the light reaches the earth. In addition to being fainter it is also redder. So effective is the interstellar material that rather small amounts of this dust are most efficient in dimming the light of the stars.

This effect can be seen on earth when a locomotive passes by with smoke pouring from its stack. Although the weight of the smoke is negligible, the smoke particles are exceedingly effective in hiding from view what lies behind it.

As a result of the dust clouds, astronomers could penetrate space only in those places where dust was absent. At all other places the dust presented an inpenetrable wall. How do the scientists get around this wall?

In 1931 Dr. Karl Jansky, of the Bell Telephone Laboratories, was investigating means of improving radio reception across the Atlantic Ocean. During his researches he discovered that radio signals or, to be more precise, radio noise like the background noise

Fig. 11-3 The 300-foot transit radio telescope of the National Radio Astronomy Observatory.

of a radio receiver, was coming from the sky. As the interpretation of this noise was not his problem, he completed his work and ignored the celestial radio signals. However, a few years later Grote Reber, a radio amateur, undertook to develop receivers to detect these noises and eventually built the first radio telescope. His early work clearly showed that intense radio signals were coming from the heart of the Milky Way. However, before his work could be completed, World War II came and research in this field ground to a halt.

After the war astronomers began in earnest to listen in on the sky. Progress both here and abroad indicated that the sky was a fertile field for observations using newly developed radio techniques.

RADIO ASTRONOMY

When radio telescopes were pointed to the sky it was discovered that the radio signals had a range in wavelength from about one-third of an inch to about 70 feet or from a frequency of 15 to 30,000 megacycles. If the entire electromagnetic spectrum is considered a piano keyboard with 60 octaves, a single octave represents the visual window by which the astronomer sees and explores space. However, with the discovery of radio signals coming from space, the radio window encompassed 12 octaves. Scientists could explore the sky with their receivers and tune them to respond to different signals.

Jansky had used a frequency of about 20 megacycles, that is, 15 meters, with which he found a strong source of radio signals in Sagittarius, the center of the galaxy. Reber, in his exploration of the galaxy, used a much shorter wavelength—about nine centimeters. It can readily be seen that this wavelength is so much greater than the wavelength of visible light that dust in the galaxy did not affect the signals coming from the distant objects. Thus scientists suddenly found something which rendered dust in space transparent and permitted deep penetration of space in all directions.

Beginning with objects close to the earth, scientists discovered that radio signals were emitted by the sun. On a normal day these signals made a sort of sizzling or frying noise. However, at the time of a solar flare the radio noise was suddenly increased in volume about a million times. Curiously, scientists were not surprised by the radio signals coming from the sun though they were astounded by the intensity of the signals at the time of a flare.

Radio telescopes turned to Venus and Jupiter also disclosed that the planets were broadcasting on their own private frequencies. This slightly surprised astronomers, for although Venus is hotter than the earth and has a dense cloud cover, there really is no reason to suspect radio waves being generated on the planet. Likewise Jupiter appeared to be an unlikely source. The reason for this is that Jupiter is so cold. It is believed that the source of this radio noise may lie deep beneath the cloud layers on the giant planet. Even the moon and Mars appeared to be a source of radio signals. Thus scientists suddenly found that many objects in the solar system were alive in a radio sense.

In 1944 Dr. H. C. van de Hulst had predicted that, because of the predominance of hydrogen in the universe, there should be a 21-centimeter wavelength emission by hydrogen atoms. Also, because hydrogen was so plentiful, it should come from all parts of the sky. In 1951 Dr. H. E. Ewen and Dr. E. M. Purcell, of Harvard, actually found this emission, and in the next ten years the entire sky was to be explored to uncover these sources.

The reason for the 21-centimeter emission lies in the peculiar behavior of the hydrogen atom. This atom is popularly imagined to be a miniature solar system with the proton as the sun and the electron as a planet. The electron moves in certain orbits around the proton. When the electron is excited by absorbing radiation, it can jump from one orbit to another farther from the nucleus. It will remain in this new larger orbit for a hundred-millionth of a second after which it will fall back into a smaller orbit and emit a pulse of energy.

If the jump is from a large orbit to the innermost, the amount of energy the electron gives up is great and the energy manifests itself as ultraviolet radiation. If the electron cascades down through the intermediate orbits, the energy may be visible light or infrared radiation, or the wavelength may be so long that the energy appears in the radio part of the electromagnetic spectrum.

On close study, scientists found that the innermost electronic orbit is not single, but rather two orbits which are close together. To understand this we must realize that both the proton and the electron spin and, thus, produce a magnetic field. The fields can attract or repel each other, depending on the direction of spin of the electron. It is apparent that when the magnetic axis of the electron is parallel to that of the proton the system is in a higher energy state. If the spin axis of the electron flips over—and it does this about once in 11 million years—the spins are anti-parallel and the system is in a lower energy state. This means that there are really two hyper-fine energy levels in the ground state. The flipping over of the axis results in the jumping of the electron from the large orbit to the small one with an emission of a radio signal with a frequency of 1420 megacycles. Collision of the hydrogen atoms in space—about every 50 years—propels the electron into the higher energy orbit.

Like any other type of radiation this "radio light" has a certain wavelength—21 centimeters which is slightly over eight inches. Ordinary radio waves in the normal broadcast band have a wavelength of about one-half mile whereas, as we have seen, visible light has a wavelength of about 1/50,000th of an inch.

Under normal terrestrial conditions this electron axis flipping does not take place. In space where the hydrogen atoms are so thinly strewn—about a half dozen to a match box—they are so far apart that the electron will persist in a higher energy state for the 11 million years required for the transition to materialize. For this reason the 21-centimeter radiation pours onto the earth from all parts of space.

The trick in making this radiation disclose the structure of the Milky Way lies in the width of the signal recorded by the radio receiver. In the case of the 21-centimeter radiation the random motions of the hydrogen atoms contribute to a certain width of the emission line. This is the *Doppler shift*. The hydrogen atoms moving toward the earth broaden the line toward the higher end of the energy scale, whereas those atoms moving away from the earth broaden it toward the lower energy part of the spectrum.

Our Milky Way has a differential rotation. The part which lies closer to the hub of the system rotates more rapidly than those farther away. Thus, if we know what area we are observing, astronomical data can make available the speeds of these regions. Therefore, if we wish to observe a region near the center of the galaxy because it has a higher speed than the sun, our signal peak will no longer be tuned to the 21-centimeter wavelength. Maximum signal strength will occur at a slightly shorter wavelength. Similarly, in observing regions farther from the center than the sun, maximum signal strength will occur at a slightly longer wavelength. Thus the shift in frequency provides a probing tool into the far reaches of the Milky Way. The structure of the Milky Way can be explored in depth using this technique.

This new method renders invisible the near clouds of hydrogen which astronomers do not want to explore and renders visible those clouds of hydrogen which may be tens of thousands of light-years away. This means that astronomers can investigate the Milky Way layer by layer to arrive at the over-all structure.

The radio telescope has been able to penetrate to vast distances and in a sense has been "bird-dogging" for the giant optical telescopes. Only recently has there been teamwork between the two instruments. As a result of this the most distant object in the known universe was discovered.

In 1950 radio astronomers at Cambridge, England discovered a source of strong signals in the constellation of Boötes, the Bear Driver. The resolution of this radio telescope was rather poor so the precise location could not be pin-pointed. However, the use of a new radio telescope at Cambridge combined with the 90-foot instrument at the California Institute of Technology permitted the radio source to be accurately located. Within a few months—in July 1960—the late Dr. Rudolph Minkowski, of the Mt. Palomar Observatory, trained the 200-inch Hale telescope in the indicated direction and with a two-hour exposure was fortunate enough to photograph a faint, fuzzy spot of light. This object—a single galaxy or system of stars or a pair of galaxies in collision—was verified as the source of the radio noise. What was most important was that Dr. Minkowski was able to obtain spectra of the object and an analysis indicated that it is receding from the earth at a speed of 90,000 miles per second—one-half the speed of light!

Thus in a single photographic series astronomers succeeded in almost tripling the known size of the universe and in doing so acquired a powerful mechanism to re-evaluate cosmological theory. The distance to the farthest galaxy before this discovery was approximately two billion light-years. The radio source in Bootes is at a distance of six billion light-years.

Some astronomers believe that this new technique will provide some of the answers which will permit an insight into the structure of the universe. Since the discovery by the late Edwin Hubble in 1926 that the galaxies were receding from us with speeds proportional to their distances, we have imagined the universe to be an expanding one. Opposed to this is a theory proposed by a British group of astute astronomers who insist that our universe is in a steady state, that is, it never had a beginning and there will be no ending. They believe the universe simply goes along always the same with every part of the universe very much like every other part.

One way of resolving this conflict would be to find a gradual difference in the galaxies as they become more distant from the earth. A galaxy a billion light-years away is photographed in light that is a billion years old. Essentially that galaxy is the way it was a billion years ago. If we can find some variation because of distance, a definitive answer may result as to the evolution of the universe. A preliminary survey of the sky indicates that the density of radio sources does increase with distance. If this is verified, and encounters which give rise to these radio sources were more frequent in the past, this would argue against the steady-state universe. This bit of evidence indicates that the evolutionary theory may be the correct one. To penetrate space to greater distances, larger telescopes must be built and chances are we will never build a large enough radio telescope to compare with the precision of the optical ones.

The University of Manchester's steerable 250-foot radio telescope at Jodrell Bank has proven one of the important instrumental advances of the century. Many significant discoveries and space-age applications have resulted from its use. Unfortunately, even though it is gargantuan in size, it still does not compare in resolving power with our optical telescopes.

It has been estimated that a radio telescope to match the resolving power of the eye would have to use a dish ten miles across. This is a ridiculous size. Although a ten-mile dish will not be built, a 600-foot radio telescope was begun and may yet be built at Sugar Grove, West Virginia. This giant radio telescope may, like the 200-inch Hale optical telescope, mark the end of the line in steerable radio telescopes.

Radio signals from space are very weak. It is estimated that they are only a hundred-millionth as strong as the television signal you

Fig. 11-4 The orbiting astronomical observatory.

Illus.: General Features Corp.

receive at home. Thus large antennas to pick up these faint signals are a necessity.

In addition to the large dishes there is also a necessity for superbly designed and constructed amplifiers to amplify the signals. Masers, super-cooled with liquid helium, are now being used to avoid all thermal noises in the amplifiers so that what is amplified is just the signal coming from space and not extraneous and background noises.

With the dawn of space travel new techniques are coming into play which will aid astronomers in their celestial researches. Soon after World War II rocket probes were launched which brought back spectra of the sun in the far ultraviolet region. Later a balloon-supported, solar telescope was launched which brought back significant, high resolution pictures of the solar surface. For the first

Fig. 11-5 The astronomical observatory on the moon. This will represent the first observatory on a stable extra terrestrial body.

Illus.: General Features Corp.

time consistent photographs showing the tiny grains comprising the visible layers of the sun became available.

With the launching of an Orbiting Astronomical Observatory, our instruments will for the first time be completely above the atmosphere of the earth, and the light messages their receivers record will be pure and undefiled. Astronomers will be able to penetrate space using the entire electromagnetic spectrum. The satellite observatory will provide leads to future exploration of the solar system and perhaps beyond that to the exploration of the stars.

Until this time, the tools of the astronomers have proven inadequate to cope with the enormous problems of interpreting what they see in space. When astronomers put their observatory on a satellite or, better yet, on the moon, a new era will dawn in this science.

CHAPTER 12

Satellites and Probes

WE HAVE BECOME quite sophisticated about launching satellites. Within a few years after the first one was successfully orbited, it was possible to place satellites in precise orbits so that perigee and apogee were within a few miles of the prescribed values. New and complex mechanisms were developed to provide precise cutoff velocities of the rocket engines and to provide precise injection angles.

Satellites were then put into "parking" orbits to circle the earth for significant periods and then be activated either to return to the earth or, in the case of a planetary probe, to take off for a planet. Launchings going far beyond the earth were called probes because, in essence, they were not satellites in the sense that they would return to a close approach of the earth. Rather, they were developed to perform a certain mission such as exploring bodies other than the earth. In some cases they could be considered "flybys"—that is, probes which simply passed by a body like a planet and then continued on their prescribed paths without returning to the earth. In other cases returnable probes were launched which traveled to a distant object and then returned close to the earth to telemeter back significant information about the remote object. The Russian Lunik III was an example of the latter type of probe.

To understand more fully probes and their missions, let's discuss orbits once more. Previously we discovered that when the rocket engines stopped firing the satellite had to return to the precise point where the engines stopped. If the velocity at the cutoff point was less than circular velocity, this point in space marked the apogee. Since this is the farthest point from the earth, as the satellite continued around the earth it had to come closer. Halfway around the earth from where the engines stopped firing we would find the nearest approach to the earth, perigee.

Now consider what takes place when the velocity is greater than circular velocity. In this case, depending on the excess of velocity, the cutoff point is perigee, and apogee will be at some distant point from the earth. The greater the excess of velocity the higher will the satellite rise until a velocity of about 36,000 feet per second is achieved. At this velocity the apogee point will theoretically be at an infinite distance from the earth. The reason why it is not at an infinite distance is that the gravitational pull of the sun is ever present, and this attraction warps the path of the satellite so that it cannot escape from the sun but is constrained to pursue a closed path around the sun like a miniature planet. Several of these

Fig. 12-1 Model of Lunik III interplanetary station.

Illus.: Sovfoto

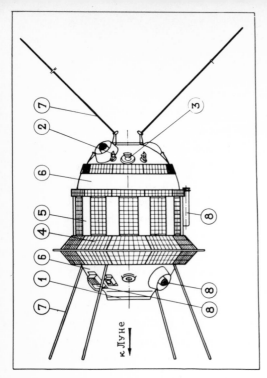

Fig. 12-2 Diagram of Lunik III interplanetary station.
1) Porthole for cameras.
2) Control jets for orientation.
3) Solar transducer.
4) Solar cells.
5) Shutters for thermal regulation.
6) Thermal screens.
7) Antennae.
8) Instruments.

Illus.: Sovfoto

escape satellites or probes have been launched to be captured by the gravitational field of the sun to circle it forever.

Scientists can deliberately warp the path of an object to make it fulfill a particular mission. Thus they can have a probe swing around the moon. They can make a probe pass close to Mars or Venus, and, relay the information it acquired back to the earth. These trajectories have been diligently developed and analyzed on giant computers and, as a result of these studies, scientists can attempt many special missions in space.

LUNAR PROBES

The nearness of the moon means that it will be subject to more attention than any other body in the solar system. Because of studies made on lunar trajectories it is possible to describe precisely what must be done to impact the moon, circle the moon and return to the earth or become a satellite of the moon.

On September 13, 1959 the Russian Lunik II impacted the

Fig. 12-3 Model of Soviet Cosmic Rocket Lunik II.

Illus.: Sovfoto

moon in the Mare Imbrium region south of a line drawn through the craters Aristillus and Autolycus and not too far from the Apennine Mountain range. On impact, Lunik II raised a dust cloud some 35 miles high that was seen by observers elsewhere than in the Soviet Union. To achieve this impact meant that the velocity had to be held within a variation either way of ten feet per second and the injection angle into its trajectory within two or three minutes of arc.

On October 10, 1959 Lunik III circled the moon and relayed back pictures of *half* the hidden side of the moon. The probe was fired almost at the time of the new moon which meant the normally hidden side of the moon was illuminated by the sun. When the probe moved around to the hidden side, it photographed this illuminated side to telemeter the pictures back to the earth later. In this case the probe had to change its orientation in mid-course. It is believed that both the sun and the moon provided the fixed points for realignment.

Some early American attempts at the moon were to have a probe circle the moon as a satellite. Under this condition, and given an adequate transmitter, a continuous set of pictures could be relayed to the earth. Here, mid-course guidance and additional rocket power are necessary to execute the maneuver.

In the case of planetary probes, devices are launched at certain optimum times when the planet is in the proper position with respect to the earth. When the probe is launched it is headed in the precise direction and given the proper speed. The Russians, in their disappointing Venus probe, actually put this into a parking orbit around the earth and some time later launched the probe from the parking orbit to head for the planet. The Russian Venus probe was a failure in terms of recovered information because the radio system went dead soon after launch.

Since the Russians do not talk about their devices or objectives, the only ones which can be described in detail are the American probes. At the time of this writing there are roughly six probes proposed to be used on six different types of missions. Although the instrumentation to gather scientific information may be the same for many of the probes, the end result will be quite different.

PROJECT RANGER

The first of the American lunar landing probes is the Ranger series. These are destined to land on the moon in what scientists call a modified "hard" landing.

While the Ranger vehicles may vary in payload and objective, there are certain elements which will be common to all. The Ranger vehicles will be relaying back pictures to the earth as they fall toward the moon and they will undertake experiments exploring some facets of lunar problems.

The objective of this series can be put in its proper perspective by discussing a particular Ranger probe—Ranger 5—which was launched on October 18, 1962 and failed to achieve its goal.

The Ranger was launched by an Atlas-Agena B rocket system from Cape Canaveral. After an intricate series of maneuvers it was asked to:

1) Leave the earth with a velocity of 24,500 miles per hour from a parking orbit at an altitude of 105 miles and then be directed on an orbit which would arrive at the moon some 240,000 miles away.

2) Perform a maneuver in space to lock onto the sun and then onto the earth.

3) Accept correction commands from the earth some 16 hours after launch, change its orientation in flight and fire a

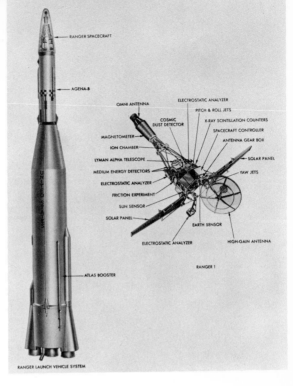

Fig. 12-4 Launch vehicle and instrumentation detail of Ranger.

Illus.: Courtesy NASA

38-pound mid-course rocket motor to place itself on collision course with the moon.

4) Reestablish its lock on the sun and the earth.

5) Perform a terminal maneuver when it came to within 5,000 miles of the moon.

6) Take television pictures of the lunar surface as it approached the moon.

7) Observe the radar reflection characteristics of the lunar surface.

8) Separate a retrorocket and capsule system from the spacecraft at approximately 68,000 feet above the lunar surface.

9) Fire a retrorocket to slow the capsule system from 6,000 miles per hour to zero velocity some 1,100 feet above the surface of the moon.

10) Detach an instrumented capsule containing a 50-pound seis-

mometer from the retrorocket so that it rough lands, with a speed under 150 miles per hour after free fall from approximately 1,100 feet. Make certain it survives the landing, positions itself and then transmits for 30 days or more, information on moon quakes and meteoritic impact.

The Ranger spacecraft, looking like a four-sided derrick-shaped vehicle on a six-sided base, stands about eight feet high and is about five feet in diameter. At escape it will weigh 750 pounds when it begins its trip which will take from 66 to 70 hours. The two solar panels contain 8,680 solar cells which can furnish about 140 watts of energy to the power pack.

When the spacecraft is 2,600 miles above the lunar surface and 35 minutes from the impact time the television cameras will go into operation. These will transmit over 100 pictures taken at the rate of one every 13 seconds. These will be relayed immediately to the earth. The screen will be coarse compared to that of our normal television sets since the scanning will be at the rate of 200 lines, less than half that of our home screens. The first pictures relayed back to the earth will cover 40 square miles on a side. But

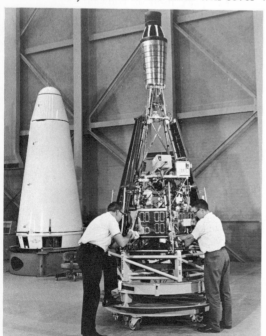

Fig. 12-5 Ranger probe under construction.

Illus.: Courtesy NASA

the detail on this 1,600-square mile area will be limited. However, as the cameras approach closer to the lunar surface the last picture will be taken from an altitude of 80,000 feet. The last picture of the moon will cover 2,000 square yards on a side. Thus the entire screen will be taken up by a picture of the moon with an area of perhaps 1½ square miles, and significant information concerning the lunar surface will be realized. The final pictures from the moon will differentiate objects on the order of 20 feet in diameter.

The list of experiments to be undertaken include gamma ray measurements, radar reflectivity of the lunar surface, lunar photographs and, finally, lunar seismic activity and meteoritic impacts.

PROJECT MARINER

After the successful landings of the Ranger spacecraft the Mariner interplanetary *flybys* were to have been launched. Strangely, the failures of the first five Rangers delayed the landing of a lunar probe so that we have successfully accomplished a planetary flyby mission with Venus as the target before a successful landing on the moon.

On August 27, 1962, Mariner 2, a hastily assembled, low weight spacecraft was launched from Cape Canaveral on a 109-day, 181,000,000-mile journey to Venus. While the normal Mariner spacecraft was to have used an Atlas-Centaur launch vehicle, the failure of the Centaur system to become operational in time forced NASA scientists to substitute a vehicle with approximately half the scheduled 1,000 pound payload for the Venus mission.

On December 14, Mariner 2 passed within 21,500 miles of the surface of the planet and collected significant information concerning interplanetary space and planetary temperatures. By an ingenious arrangement of microwave and infra-red radiometers a temperature profile was obtained from the probe.

Mariner 2 represented the most successful interplanetary space probe ever undertaken. Its pioneering efforts are destined to affect all future planetary probes and for that reason Mariner 2 can be assumed to be the prototype for all other Mariner probes.

Fig. 12-6 Mariner passing Venus.

Illus.: General Features Corp.

The spacecraft at launch weighed 446 pounds of which but 40 pounds represented scientific experiments. The solar panels, which when unfurled, measured 16.5 feet across contained 9,800 solar cells which could furnish a maximum of 222 watts of power. A 1,000-watt-hour silver zinc storage battery provided power during peak power demands. A 50-pound-thrust mid-course correction rocket system and associated electronics elements were also included.

At launch the spacecraft started out well, but without the mid-course correction, the probe would have missed the planet by about 250,000 miles. To correct for this deviation, about 80 miles per hour of velocity had to be added to the Mariner's speed. At 8.73 days after launch, when the probe was about 1,500,000 miles from the earth, the mid-course motor was fired and this resulted in the probe coming within 21,500 miles of the planet on December 14, when it was about 36,000,000 miles from the earth.

Experimental results of Mariner 2:

A solar plasma experiment using a single electrostatic spectrometer revealed that one of the principal results was that there is a measurable flow of plasma from the sun at speeds of from 200 to 500 miles per second with a temperature of about one million degrees F. Only 10 to 20 protons and electrons per cubic inch are in this solar wind.

There was no evidence of a Venusian magnetic field though one with a value of as minute as 4 gamma could have been detected. This compares with a value of 30,000 gamma at the earth's equator. The lack of a magnetic field at the flyby distance means there were no magnetically trapped particles and thus Venus could not possess radiation belts. These findings are consistent with the theory of planetary magnetism in that a high rate of rotation is necessary for a magnetic field.

No impacts of cosmic dust occurred near the flyby of the Mariner probe. However, in the 1,700 hours of reduced data, two impacts were recorded despite the fact that tiny particles weighing but one-trillionth of a pound could have been detected. The number of particles recorded near Venus were about 0.1% that recorded near the earth. One preliminary conclusion is that because of particles blasted off the moon as a result of meteoritic impacts there are about 1,000 times as many particles near the earth as near Venus. Tracking studies of the probe gave rise to surprising results. Because Venus has no satellite its mass has been most difficult to determine. However, the change in the motion of the Mariner 2 probe under the influence of the gravitational field of the planet and the resulting change in the transmitted radio signals indicated that the mass of Venus is 0.814585 times that of the earth with an error of less than 0.015%. This is the most precise value ever determined for the mass of this planet. The precise location of the tracking station to within 20 yards compared to the 100 yards known previously was made possible in this fashion. Other by-products may be the better determination of the astronomical unit and the mass of the earth's moon.

The results from the microwave and infrared radiometers indicate that the planet is covered by dense clouds which have a temperature of -30 degrees F. The microwave radiometer indicated that the surface temperature of the planet was about 800 degrees F. Apparently no radiation is transmitted to the clouds from the surface.

PROJECT SURVEYOR

Along with the Mariner there is being developed a series of lunar probes which will be "soft-landed" to permit a full complement of instruments to settle onto the lunar surface. The first of these soft-landed probes will be the Surveyor.

Scientists contemplate using an Atlas-Centaur (or possibly a Titan II or Saturn C-1) launch vehicle for this probe. The pay-

Fig. 12-7 Surveyor approaching lunar landing.

Illus.: General Features Corp.

load for this system will weigh approximately 2500 pounds. Of this total, from 60% to 75% will comprise the fuel for the retro-rockets to slow the payload so the touchdown speed will be on the order of 10 to 20 miles per hour. The trip to the moon is scheduled to take about 66 hours.

Firing of the retrorockets constitutes a critical maneuver. Scientists contemplate the final landing to be made with a liquid-propellant, variable-thrust rocket, modulated by a closed-loop guidance system. In this type of landing the retrorockets destroy most of the downward velocity to slow the vehicle, and the variable downward push of the engine is controlled by inputs such as altitude, initial velocity, etc.

On the final approach to the lunar surface the spent, main retro-rocket will be jettisoned. Small vernier rockets will be used for last-minute corrections to the course to insure landing at approximately the desired impact point.

The Surveyor space craft will be supported by three legs and will stand 11 feet high. Like the Mariners, it will house a sun seeker to orient the solar-cell paddles for power and a directional antenna which will always be beamed at the earth for communications.

The total landing weight of the system will be about 750 pounds, of which 250 pounds will be scientific instrumentation. The remaining 500 pounds will be communications equipment and temperature control instrumentation to protect the instruments from the −240-degree cold of the lunar night and the near boiling point temperatures during the day.

The instrument complex will contain a complete system for investigations of the lunar surface and subsurface. It will house a sensitive magnetometer to determine the extent of the lunar magnetic field—if indeed one exists. There will be instruments to measure the gravitational field of the moon which may yield a better value of the moon's mass. There will be a drill which will bore through the surface to bring up samples of the moon from at least 18 inches deep. Instruments will measure the radiation falling to the moon as well as the extent of the lunar atmosphere. A delicate seismometer will be included to record earthquakes. A meteoritic impact counter will be sent along to record the rate of fall of solid particles to the lunar surface. Finally, a spectrometer will go along to analyze the lunar surface materials.

This complex of instruments will need a stable and reliable power source. There are several possibilities and three power sources are planned for the vehicle.

The first will be a complex of solar cells to pick up the sun's radiation for conversion to energy. Some of this energy will be stored in batteries which are carried aloft as the second source. The third item is a nuclear power supply—perhaps a SNAP system (Satellite Nuclear Auxiliary Power) to be sent along to augment the solar power supply.

The major component of the Surveyor will be a multiple-camera television system to relay to the earth pictures of the lunar surface and subsurface. As the vehicle approaches the moon the television system will go into operation and will survey the lunar surface prior to the landing. Once the probe is down the television cameras will scan the lunar panorama through 360°. When the drill goes into operation, small fragments of the moon's surface and subsurface will be brought up to the vehicle. There they will be scanned by television and a chemical analysis will also be performed. This television operation will be monitored so that scientists at the Goldstone Tracking Station will observe the performance of the semi-automatic analyzer on their television screens.

PROJECT PROSPECTOR

There is one limitation to the Surveyor program. When the Surveyor sets down on the moon, the lunar materials to be analyzed will be those directly beneath the probe. Thus, if the area is not representative of the lunar surface, the results obtained will not give a true picture of the physical characteristics of the lunar surface. There is a way to get around this—send a mobile probe to the moon to wander over the lunar surface.

Fig. 12-8   Prospector traversing lunar surface.

Illus.: General Features Corp.

When advanced Saturn launch vehicles are available, we may include a mobile lunar probe in our program. It will be a wheeled or tracked vehicle with long booms both front and back to prevent overturning in going over steep grades or inclines. The soft landing of a vehicle of this shape represents a major problem to its planners.

Once on the moon, the instruments can perform a variety of investigations. The mobility of this controllable spacecraft means that it can determine the texture, hardness and character of the lunar surface over perhaps a 100-mile range. It will conduct temperature studies over this area. It can determine the temperature change with depth and the thermal conductivity of the lunar layers as the vehicle travels over the surface.

Before painting too optimistic a picture of what the mobile probe might do for science, it may be well to point out that because of the tremendous impetus given to getting a man on the moon this project may be completely by-passed or may be re-designed as a more direct aid to manned exploration.

PROJECT VOYAGER

At about the same time we hope to put a mobile probe on the moon, scientists are contemplating unmanned planetary orbiters. These are designed to fill in the gaps in our knowledge concerning planetary surfaces. To fulfill this mission scientists have proposed Project Voyager.

Again the booster for this project will be an advanced Saturn called Saturn C-1B. Only with this giant can the necessary payloads be given escape velocity and then furnished with sufficient fuel so that maneuvers can be undertaken in the vicinity of a planet. Since the goal is a planetary orbiter, or lander, both retrorockets and terminal guidance systems are necessary. The greater weight of these probes will permit the planet seeker to "home in" on the planet and guide it into an orbit to make it a planet satellite.

Because Voyager has similar missions, it may not look too different from the Ranger or Mariner vehicles. Like these it will contain a complex of instruments for detecting radiations, particles, plasma and other characteristics of interplanetary space. However, its true mission will take shape on approach to the target planet.

Venus and Mars are the goals for this project. Venus, whose orbit lies within that of the earth, comes within 26 million miles of the earth. Mars lies outside the orbit of the earth and at its nearest approach is about 34 million miles distant. Thus to get a substantial payload to these planets will require not only tremendous boosters but also long time intervals.

Because Venus is completely shrouded by clouds, Voyager will use active radar for mapping the surface. Eventually it may be possible to discover the nature of the Venusian surface. Because of the detection of water vapor in the atmosphere from balloon observations from earth, it was considered possible that large amounts of water may be present. Were it not for the 800°F. surface temperatures recently measured by the Mariner 2 probe, this feature would indicate to astronomers the exciting possibility that a life of some sort may be present on Venus.

Following Venus, Mars is the target. Unlike Venus, we can see the surface of Mars. Thus the objective in this orbiter will be to photograph the planetary surface and relay these details to the earth.

It is contemplated that systems for culturing micro-organisms and measuring changes in a culture medium may be landed on Mars. Also contemplated is a television system for relaying to the earth pictures from microscopes working in the ultraviolet and near ultraviolet regions of the spectrum. Definitive answers to the extent of life forms and their characteristics may be derived from this investigation. We hope that with Project Voyager another chapter will be added to our book of knowledge concerning the planets.

PROJECT APOLLO

No matter what we believe probes can do for us, it is unreasonable to assume that they can replace a man in space. Consequently, tremendous emphasis has been placed on Project Apollo—that of getting a three-man crew to the moon. Although guarded language is being used to describe what the scientists would like to do, nevertheless this project has achieved the highest priority.

One objective of this program is to place a three-man crew in orbit for periods up to two months. It is from this experience that scientists hope to build on missions which will take a man farther from the earth and for longer periods of time. Circumlunar flights, lunar orbital flights and, finally, a manned landing on the moon are the goals.

In this project the "building block" technique will be incorporated with three complementary components making up the orbiting vehicle. The most critical component will be the central command module. This would house the crew during the launch and re-entry phases of flight; it would serve also as the flight control center for the remainder of the mission. The command module would serve as an earth orbiter or a circumlunar orbiter. When orbiting the earth it could be employed as a laboratory to execute needed studies of the space environment.

The propulsion module could be used for circumlunar missions

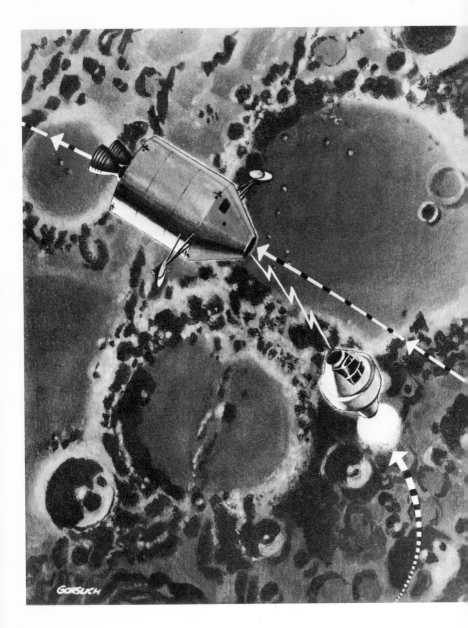

Fig. 12-9   Return of lunar landing "bug."

Illus.: General Features Corp.

where mid-course corrections are necessary. In earth-orbital missions it could provide maneuverability to permit orbit modification or rendezvousing with other space craft. At launch it may be used to provide a safe landing for astronauts in the event of an aborted mission.

The mission module would simply comprise an assembly containing instruments devoted to a specific mission. Thus, for various missions, only the mission module would be sent up to rendezvous with the astronauts already in orbit.

Project Apollo is a bold concept, and the success of this venture will eventually achieve for the scientist his next great goal—the moon.

CHAPTER 13

Methods of Propelling Space Vehicles

In Chapter 3 we discussed Newton's first and second laws of motion and the important corollary to the second law known as the law of conservation of momentum. It was also noted that the first law was merely a special case of the more general second law.

NEWTON'S THIRD LAW OF MOTION

The third law may also be considered a corollary of the second law, since it can be directly deduced from it.

Suppose that two astronauts in space suits are motionless in empty space with no forces acting on them. Since no external force is acting on them they cannot experience any acceleration as a system. (Since $F = 0$; ma must also equal zero.) However, suppose that they face each other, draw up their legs, place the soles of their boots together, and kick. They will, of course, move away from each other as a result of the thrust of their legs. If they are of equal mass they will experience equal accelerations and will recede from each other with equal velocities relative to their original position in space.

Since no external force is acting, the sum of the two forces which accelerated the astronauts in opposite directions must be zero. Otherwise a net force would have been generated which would give the whole system a net acceleration. From the second law this could not occur without an external force. Thus the two forces must be equal in magnitude and opposite in direction; i.e.,

$$F = -F \quad \text{or} \quad F + F = 0$$

The above is a mathematical expression of Newton's third law which can be stated as follows: "For every action there is an equal and opposite reaction." The word "action" here means applied force. The word "reaction" means reaction force.

Now suppose that one of the astronauts is replaced by an inert object of equal mass. If the remaining astronaut kicks with equal force, the separation velocity will be the same as before. Thus the inert object exerts a passive reaction force exactly equal to the kick of the second astronaut.

Suppose now that the mass of the astronaut is 200 pounds (6.2 slugs) and he exerts sufficient force to propel the inert mass away from him at a separation velocity of 20 feet per second. The velocity of the astronaut relative to his original position is ten feet per second, and the velocity of the inert mass is equal in magnitude and opposite in direction. We can say that the astronaut is employing a propulsion system—a very crude rocket. The inert mass kicked away by the astronaut would be called "reaction mass" or "expellant." It would have an "exhaust velocity" of 20 feet per second and the "burn-out velocity" of the astronaut would be ten feet per second.

If the astronaut wished to improve his crude propulsion system, he might divide his store of inert expellant into two equal parts. Now, if he expels 100 pounds at the same exhaust velocity of 20 feet per second, he will find that the inert mass leaves the initial position at 15 feet per second while he and the remaining 100 pounds have acquired a velocity of only five feet per second. (This can be checked by applying the law of conservation of momentum; thus, $100 \times 15 = 300 \times 5$.) However, when he repeats the process with the second half of the expellant, the division of velocities will be more favorable. Of the total separation velocity of 20 feet per second, he will get a full third, or 6.67 feet per second. Thus he has acquired a total velocity change or "burn-out velocity" of 11.67 feet per second rather than ten feet per second as with the first method.

If he continued to divide the expellant into smaller and smaller pieces, his system would continue to improve until finally he would be firing the mass out as individual atoms. Then his velocity could be found from the fundamental propulsion equation (to be derived in Appendix 1):

$$v = c \ln \frac{G}{E}$$

where v is the burn-out velocity, c is exhaust velocity, G is initial or gross mass, E is empty mass and $\ln$ refers to the natural logarithm. In this case, $c = 20$ feet per second, $G = 400$ pounds and $E = 200$ pounds. Thus,

$$\frac{G}{E} = 2 \quad \text{and} \quad \ln \frac{G}{E} = \ln 2 = 0.691$$

Thus,

$$V = 0.691 \times 20 = 13.8 \text{ feet per second}$$

Do not be concerned about understanding this equation now. Simply note that the process of dividing the expellant into smaller chunks leads to higher final velocity for the same exhaust velocity. We were able to demonstrate this easily for the case where the expellant is divided into two parts. By the same process, it can be shown that the final velocity for three parts is 12.33 feet per second. If we continue to divide the expellant into smaller parts, we will find that at five parts the burn-out velocity is 12.91 feet per second, at ten parts it is 13.34 feet per second and at N parts it is

$$v_{BO} = v_s \left[\frac{1}{2 \times 1} + \frac{1}{4 \times 3} + \frac{1}{6 \times 5} + \cdots + \frac{1}{2N (2N - 1)} \right]$$

where v_{BO} is the final velocity and v_s is the separation or exhaust velocity.

Comparing the equation above with $v = c \ln (G/E)$ we can see that the series inside the brackets will equal ln 2 when $N = \infty$, that is, when $m = 0$. Actually, the molecules of gas in the exhaust of a rocket are so small compared to the mass of a rocket that we can assume they are actually of zero mass and use the logarithm form. In fact, if we carried out the series to about 20 steps, the answer would be close enough for most purposes. At ten steps the error is only about three per cent.

Note that the final velocity was increased simply by dividing the expellant into smaller chunks while continuing to use the same exhaust velocity. Now suppose that the same amount of energy is used to accelerate the smaller mass as was originally used when expelling the entire amount in one piece. Now the exhaust velocity will increase as the size of the chunks decreases, and there will be two factors contributing to a higher final velocity. Of course the total energy expended will be higher in this case, but that is not necessarily a detriment. In a nuclear rocket, for example, there is plenty of energy available. So we find that the best expellant material to use is hydrogen—since hydrogen atoms have the lowest mass of any of the elements.

TYPES OF PROPULSION SYSTEMS

All known propulsion systems, and in fact all of which we can clearly conceive (leaving out such things as psychic or non-physical systems), act according to Newton's third law of motion. There must always be some reaction mass which acquires a momentum equal and opposite to that of the moving object. This applies to any accelerated object of any kind.

Those who questioned the ability of a rocket to operate in a vacuum were correct in saying that, "It must have something to push against." They were wrong in not realizing that it could carry reaction mass—something to push against—along with it.

Most of the propulsion systems familiar to us on the earth

depend on external reaction mass. For most aircraft, the reaction mass is the air. For trains and automobiles, it is the earth itself. All such systems will be called *extrinsic* propulsion systems since the reaction mass is derived from a source external to the vehicle. The rocket carries its reaction mass internally. We will call such systems *intrinsic* propulsion systems.

We could classify all propulsion systems in these two categories except that we must also consider the source of propulsive energy. Again, this is sometimes carried internally and is sometimes available externally to the vehicle. Thus, we have four basic types of systems which we can call extrinsic-extrinsic, or E^2, extrinsic-intrinsic, or EI and I^2 and IE systems. In all four cases the reaction mass is considered first.

All "physically" possible systems (again leaving out systems which go beyond physics as we now understand it) can be listed in one of these four categories. However, there are some additional subcategories which must be given special attention.

In this section we list a number of types of extrinsic and intrinsic systems with only very brief explanation. The major types of propulsion will be examined in more detail in later sections.

EXTRINSIC—EXTRINSIC SYSTEMS

A good example of the E^2-type of propulsion system is that of the sail boat. The reaction mass is the air and the energy source is the kinetic energy of the air molecules.

An analogous system proposed for space flight is the solar sail: it would be propelled by radiation pressure from the sun. Again the reaction mass is external and the energy source is the kinetic energy of the reaction mass itself.

The recombination ramjet has been proposed for use in the upper atmosphere. This system would scoop up gas molecules which had been ionized by the sun—for example, ozone, atomic oxygen, etc.—and make use of the energy released as these ions recombined into stable molecules. The reaction mass would, of course, be the recombined molecules.

An analogous system has been proposed for interplanetary and even interstellar flight. This is the interplanetary ramjet. It would scoop up the hydrogen atoms which occur in low concentration even in "empty" space and use them to sustain a hydrogen fusion reaction. This energy would then be used to expel the reaction product, helium, from the rear of the ship. Of course this is purely theoretical, as are many of the systems to be listed here. We have not yet learned how to produce any fusion reaction except that of the hydrogen bomb.

Other possible E^2 systems include a solar-powered ramjet, or a ramjet operated on power transmitted from an artificial external source—radar transmitter. Of course, bullets fired from guns, arrows and all types of projectiles are E^2 systems.

A special subcategory of the E^2 systems are what might be called the *force-field systems*. Of course all acceleration depends on the interaction of force fields of some type, but these usually operate inside the vehicle even when the reaction mass and the energy source are external. What is considered here is a large external field such as the gravitational or magnetic fields of the earth, or artificial, external fields.

In these cases the reaction mass is the earth, the sun or some other large astronomical object. Reaction against the external mass is produced through the medium of a natural or artificial force field.

If a rocket is fired close to the moon at just the right velocity, it will be captured momentarily, acquire the moon's orbital velocity and then break away again. If the initial approach speed is too low, it will impact on the moon; if too high, it will not be accelerated by the moon. However, if the speed is just right, the orbital velocity of the moon will be added to the original velocity of the rocket.

If we imagine that the moon is a large elastic sphere and the rocket is a small elastic sphere, we can visualize this addition of velocity by imagining an impact on the leading side of the moon. The rocket would be struck by the moon much as a ball is struck by a bat and the rocket would depart at higher than its original speed. The moon would lose a tiny part of its momentum during the impact. Essentially the same thing happens during the grazing encounter except that the moon and the rocket are linked by a gravity field rather than by contact. This is actually an example of *gravitic* propulsion. The force of gravity could actually be used to accelerate a rocket in this way. Since the reaction mass in this case is the moon and the source of energy is the kinetic energy of the moon and both are external to the rocket, this is an E^2 system.

Another E^2 force field might theoretically be designed using the artificial electromagnetic field of a Thompson coil.

Students of physics will be familiar with the impressive "jumping ring" experiment in which a ring of conducting metal, usually aluminum, placed around the iron core of a solenoid is thrown several feet into the air when the switch is closed and the coil activated. Whether or not such a system is ever used for catapulting full-size space ships (perhaps from the surface of the moon), it can easily be demonstrated using small-scale models.

The device operates in accordance with Lenz's law—that unlike (or anti-parallel) electric currents will repel each other. It is well known that a current in a conductor sets up a magnetic field which tends to induce a like (parallel) current in any nearby conductor. Since like currents attract we would expect any nearby conductors to be attracted to an electromagnet.

Actually, the conductor will neither be attracted nor repelled if we are using a direct-current electromagnet, since currents are only generated by changing magnetic fields. However, if the current in the coil is alternating, we will get induced currents in the aluminum ring and we will have a force exerted on the ring. It would still seem that it should be an attractive force except for one thing—the induced current lags behind the primary current. Thus it happens that by the time the induced current has reached its peak in one direction, the primary current has already reversed and is moving in the opposite direction. It is this *phase lag* that causes the repelling force which throws the ring into the air.

EXTRINSIC–INTRINSIC SYSTEMS

The EI systems are those which depend on reaction mass from their environment but carry a source of energy internally.

A good example of this type is the nuclear ramjet (Project Pluto) which carries a nuclear reactor for energy and uses air for reaction mass. Nuclear submarines are also of this type.

The chemical airbreathers—propellor, turbojet, ramjet, turbo-rocket, Liquid Air Cycle Engine (LACE), etc.—can be considered to be in this category since most of their reaction mass comes from the air. However, since only half of their energy can be said to be internal, it could be argued that they belong in the previous category or half way between.

Another EI system could theoretically be designed based on the Thompson-coil principle with a slight modification, but in this case the coil is carried within the vehicle. Now suppose that we use the ionized air of the upper atmosphere for the "ring" which has now become reaction mass rather than vehicle. The field of the coil induces a current in a mass of ionized air and repels it backward away from the vehicle, thus driving the vehicle forward. Thus the energy source is internal and the reaction mass is acquired from an external source.

INTRINSIC–INTRINSIC SYSTEMS

The I^2 category includes the classical space flight propulsion systems—the liquid chemical rockets, as well as the solid and hybrid chemical rockets, the nuclear rockets, the electric rocket with nuclear energy source (ion, plasma, colloid and arc systems) and the photon rocket. Since some of these are of major importance, they will be discussed in greater detail later.

INTRINSIC–EXTRINSIC SYSTEMS

This category, IE, includes all systems in which the mass is carried internally and the energy is obtained from outside. No present systems operate in this manner, but several have been proposed.

One class of proposed IE systems is the solar-powered space ship—either solar thermodynamic or solar electric.

In the first type solar energy is used to heat a gas, probably hydrogen, to a very high temperature. The gas is then expelled from a nozzle very much as in the nuclear rocket, the only difference being the source of energy for heating the gas.

In the second type the solar energy is used to generate electricity which is then used to expel plasma or ions from the rear of the vehicle.

Similar IE systems, either thermal or electrical, would depend on transmitted artificial power. One system very similar to the solar-powered space ship would depend on a large solar-energy collector separate from the space ship. For example, a large reflector on the moon might be used to collect and redirect solar energy toward the space ship. In this way, high-intensity solar radiation could be used without the necessity of accelerating a large and massive collector with the vehicle. A series of exploding atom bombs might be used as the source of energy rather than the sun.

Other types of electromagnetic energy might also be transmitted to the vehicle to be used for thermal or electrical acceleration of stored expellant mass. Thus radar or radio energy might be beamed to the space vehicle.

Another gravitic propulsion system, but this time using internal reaction mass and thus in the IE category, is the "kick in the perigee" system. Assume that a chemical or nuclear rocket is in an elliptical satellite orbit around the earth or some other planet and the pilot plans to expend a certain amount of propellant to accelerate from satellite velocity to something more than escape velocity, the higher the better. Does it make any difference where on the elliptical trajectory he fires his rockets? Actually it does, although it is not immediately obvious why it should. If he fires at perigee (closest point to the earth), his final velocity will be higher than if he fires at apogee or anywhere else on the trajectory. The reason for this is that the rocket will leave the gravity field of the earth faster than it entered. Thus it will be accelerated more in approaching the earth than it will be decelerated on leaving, since the approach time is greater than the departure time.

Now assume that the ellipse of the orbit is extremely long and that apogee is one million miles from the earth—the practical limit of the earth's gravitational field. At this point the vehicle velocity is very close to zero. When it has fallen into perigee near the earth, the velocity is very close to escape velocity.

Suppose, for convenience, that the exhaust velocity of the rocket happens to approximate escape velocity and that the rocket expels all of the propellant just at perigee. The final velocity of the propellant relative to the earth will be zero, and it will fall down into the atmosphere.

Finally, assume that the mass ratio of the rocket is such that its burn-out velocity or velocity change due to engine thrust would just equal its exhaust velocity (this will happen if the mass ratio is equal to the base of the natural logarithm—$e = 2.72$). Then the rocket velocity will jump from escape velocity to twice escape velocity while at perigee. What will the final velocity be at apogee?

Note that if thrust had been applied at apogee the final velocity would be that of escape. But the problem above must be solved in terms of energy—the kinetic and gravitational potential energy of the vehicle.

If we go through this exercise we will find that the final velocity of the vehicle at apogee will be 1.71 times the velocity of escape—an improvement of 71% over the value obtained by firing the engines at apogee. This increase is the result of the gravitational field of the earth acting on the vehicle and propellant, and it is therefore correct to label this a *Gravitic Propulsion System*. It should be noted that a very small velocity is applied to the earth during this maneuver and, thus, mass as well as energy is external. Therefore this is a mixed system and cannot be considered a pure IE type.

The foregoing chapter is an incomplete list of possible propulsion systems in these four arbitrary categories. The imaginative reader can probably think of some other ways in which space ships might possibly be accelerated.

CHAPTER 14

Chemical Rockets

ALL ROCKET AND jet engines in use today depend on chemical propellants for energy. The propulsion energy which accelerates the aircraft or space vehicle is derived from the chemical energy of the propellants, and the materials which make up the rocket exhaust are the products of combustion of the propellants.

THE CHEMISTRY OF PROPELLANTS

Chemical energy is released in two ways in propulsion systems: either from the decomposition of an unstable molecule such as hydrogen peroxide or through the chemical combination of reactive elements or compounds. The simplest example of the latter is the combination of hydrogen and oxygen to give water and energy.

A rocket using only hydrogen peroxide or some other unstable compound for propulsion is called a *monopropellant* rocket. Some common monopropellants other than hydrogen peroxide (H_2O_2) are hydrazine (N_2H_2) and nitromethane (CH_3NO_2). Some of the solid explosives such as nitrocellulose are also used as monopropellants.

Energy must be supplied to a monopropellant chemical during

its manufacture. This stored energy is then released as the unstable molecule decomposes in the rocket chamber.

Those who have studied chemistry recall that when hydrogen is burned in oxygen, the products are water and energy. This energy is so great that the resulting high-temperature water vapor will leave the nozzle of a properly designed rocket engine at over two miles per second. A system using two chemicals is called a *bipropellant* rocket. The two propellants are the *fuel* and *oxidizer*.

Chemists commonly symbolize the reaction of two reactive elements or compounds in a chemical equation. Thus,

$$2H_2 + O_2 \longrightarrow 2H_2O + energy$$

where the subscripts refer to the number of atoms in a molecule and the numbers preceding the chemical symbols refer to the number of molecules. Since no atoms are created or destroyed in a chemical reaction, the total number of atoms of each type must be the same after the reaction as before. Two molecules (four atoms) of hydrogen plus one molecule (two atoms) of oxygen will produce two molecules of water.

The chemical equation tells us how much of one material reacts with another. Since an atom of oxygen has eight times the mass of an atom of hydrogen and four atoms of hydrogen react with two of oxygen, we can see that eight mass units of oxygen (pounds, kilograms, slugs, etc.) will combine exactly with one unit of hydrogen with no excess of either material after the reaction. How many mass units of water will form? Obviously nine, since matter is neither created nor destroyed in the reaction.

When rocket engineers wish to impress laymen with their knowledge, they refer to this exact proportion of fuel and oxidizer as the *stoichiometric* ratio (Stoy [as in boy]-key-o-met-ric). Since this word is hard to pronounce and obviously of Greek origin (from *stoicheion*—a first principle or element) it is very useful for this purpose. It also has some value in differentiating between the theoretically optimum mixture ratio—the stoichiometric ratio—and other ratios often employed for practical reasons. Although a long word, it is nevertheless shorter than "theoretically optimum" and has a more specific meaning.

The energy released when hydrogen and oxygen combine to form water is called the *heat of formation* of water. This is equal to 124,087 Btu per mole. A Btu or British Thermal Unit is the amount of heat necessary to raise the temperature of one pound of water one degree Fahrenheit. A *mole* is a molecular weight of any material expressed in some unit of weight or mass. In this case it means 18 pounds of water.

Thus the reaction between hydrogen and oxygen will produce $124,087 \div 18 = 6900$ Btu per pound of water formed or 222,000 Btu per slug.

Now if hydrogen and oxygen combine in an idealized rocket engine to form an exhaust of water vapor, what will be the exhaust velocity? Suppose that all of the heat of formation above can be converted into kinetic energy of the exhaust. What exhaust velocity will be produced?

First we must change from heat units to units of mechanical energy. Engineers are familiar with the well-known *mechanical equivalent of heat* which refers to the amount of mechanical energy or work which can be obtained from a unit of heat energy. In English units we express this equivalence as 778 foot-pounds per Btu. It is the somewhat surprising fact that the same amount of energy that would raise the temperature of one pound of water one degree Fahrenheit would also raise the same pound of water 778 feet high! Or conversely, a pound of water would have to fall 778 feet at Niagara Falls and then transmit this energy to the hydroelectric generator in order to heat a pound of water on an electric stove only one degree! (Assuming no loss in energy.)

Thus we can calculate that the 222,000 Btu available from the formation of one slug of water (note that this is 32.2 pounds, whereas a "slug of whiskey" is only two ounces) is

$$222,000 \times 778 = 1.73 \times 10^8 \text{ foot-pounds}$$

From Chapter 3 we know that the kinetic energy of a moving

body in foot-pounds is equal to $mv^2/2$ if the mass, m, is expressed in slugs. Thus,

$$\frac{mv^2}{2} = 1.73 \times 10^8 \text{ foot-pounds}$$

and

$$\frac{v^2}{2} = 1.73 \times 10^8 \text{ foot-pounds per slug}$$

Then,

$$v^2 = 3.46 \times 10^8 \quad \text{and} \quad v = 18,600 \text{ feet per second}$$

Normally, the symbol c is used for exhaust velocity; therefore, $c = 18,800$ feet per second for our ideal hydrogen-oxygen rocket.

We can express this value as specific impulse by dividing by 32.2. This results in a value of 580 pound (mass) seconds per pound (force) which is commonly abbreviated incorrectly to 580 seconds. As explained in Chapter 2, it might clarify matters to use a new unit of velocity—the stapp—and express the result as 580 stapps. This suggested unit will be used here rather than the cumbersome pound (mass) seconds per pound (force), which combines two systems of units, or the short but incorrect "seconds."

This quantity of 18,800 feet per second is of course an ideal value. There are many unavoidable energy losses in converting the heat of formation into exhaust kinetic energy. In order to achieve such a high level of performance it would be necessary to eliminate all heat losses to the walls, all heat radiated from the rocket and all excess heat normally remaining in the hot exhaust gases. The latter is by far the greatest cause of inefficiency and an area for fruitful future work.

In practice, because of the large amount of heat remaining in the exhaust gases, the heat necessary to vaporize the liquid propellants and heat radiated away from the rocket, energy efficiency is only 50% to 60%. Thus exhaust velocity and specific impulse will be lowered by a factor of 1.41 (or the square root of two) if we use the lower figure of 50%. Instead of 580 stapps we can expect something closer to $580/1.41 = 411$ stapps.

It is expected that the Centaur hydrogen-oxygen engine will

have a vacuum I_{sp} (specific impulse) of 420 stapps, indicating a performance a little above 50% energy utilization.

Another chemical reaction basic to rocket propulson is that between carbon and oxygen. Although carbon is not used alone as a rocket fuel, this is theoretically possible and carbon is a major constituent of many fuel mixtures and compounds.

The reaction of carbon and oxygen can be expressed as

$$C + O_2 \longrightarrow CO_2 + 169{,}900 \text{ Btu}$$

Thus one mole (molecular weight expressed in pounds) or 12 pounds of carbon plus 32 pounds of oxygen react to give 44 pounds of carbon dioxide plus 169,900 Btu. Although this is even more energy than resulted from the formation of one mole of water, it is less energy per pound—only 3861 Btu per pound or 124,000 Btu per slug. This is equivalent to 9.65×10^7 foot-pounds per slug.

Now, since

$$\frac{c^2}{2} = 9.65 \times 10^7$$

then

$$c^2 = 1.93 \times 10^8$$

and

$$c = 13{,}900 \text{ feet per second}$$

which is equivalent to an I_{sp} of 430 stapps. If only half of this energy is utilized, then the result would be $c = 9850$ feet per second or $I_{sp} = 305$ stapps.

The most common liquid rocket fuel in use today is kerosene, which is a mixture of hydrocarbons similar in composition to octane, C_8H_{18}. Note that a mole of octane would have a mass of 114 pounds and would contain 96 pounds of carbon and 18 pounds of hydrogen. Thus it would be only 15.8% hydrogen and we would expect its performance to be close to that of pure carbon. In practice the vacuum specific impulse values obtained for lox (liquid oxygen) and kerosene are about 310 stapps ($c = 10{,}000$ feet per second) for high-performance systems.

Of course, the method used above can provide only a rough estimate of propulsion system performance under vacuum conditions. If we wish to obtain more accurate answers for vacuum operation or take into account the effects of atmospheric pressure, much more complex calculations must be undertaken. However, these will be left to the many excellent books now available on rocket propulsion.

Only one other situation will be investigated here. That is the case where hydrogen somehow acquires the energy of the hydrogen-oxygen reaction without carrying oxygen along in the vehicle.

In this case the heat of formation of H_2O of 124,087 Btu per mole can be applied to only two pounds of hydrogen with a resulting 62,044 Btu per pound or 2.0×10^6 Btu per slug. This is equivalent to 1.55×10^9 foot-pounds per slug. Then

$$c^2 = 2 \times 1.55 \times 10^9 = 3.10 \times 10^9 = 31 \times 10^8$$

and

$$c = 5.58 \times 10^4 \qquad I_{sp} = 1730 \text{ stapps}$$

Although this is a theoretical value and apparently an upper limit, the surprising truth is that the fuel specific impulse of jet and propellor aircraft can be even higher than this, because the air serves as "free" reaction mass as well as free oxidizer.

At high vehicle speeds the air is no longer "free" reaction mass since it must be accelerated to the vehicle's speed before it can be used. However, it is still a free oxidizer and it should be possible with future jet engines to maintain fuel specific impulse values of $1730 \div 1.41 = 1200$ stapps all the way to satellite velocity.

BASIC PROPULSION CONCEPTS

The reader should already be familiar with the terms exhaust velocity and specific impulse from the discussion in Chapter 3. In this section the terms thrust, mass flow rate and total impulse will also be considered.

In Chapter 3 we saw that Newton's second law of motion could be written $F = ma$ or $F = mv/t$. If the force to be considered is the thrust of the rocket, T, which is in turn derived from the reaction of the exhaust, then

$$T = \frac{mc}{t}$$

The quantity m/t is called the mass flow rate and is expressed in slugs per second or pounds per second in the English system. It is commonly written $\dot{m}$ (pronounced m dot), where the dot refers to division by time. Thus, $T = \dot{m}c$.

Since this is a form of Newton's second law, if m is expressed in pounds of mass, T would be in poundals of force. If we wish to express T in pounds of force, m must be in slugs.

Suppose that a rocket with a vacuum exhaust velocity of 10,000 feet per second (liquid oxygen and kerosene) burns one slug of propellants per second. What is the thrust of the engine? Obviously 10,000 pounds, since $\dot{m} = 1$. Now we find $\dot{m}$ for the Titan missile with 300,000 pounds of sea level thrust and approximately 8000 feet per second exhaust velocity under sea level burning conditions. (The Titan burns liquid oxygen and kerosene.)

$$\dot{m} = \frac{T}{c} = \frac{300,000}{8000} = 37.5 \text{ slugs per second}$$

or approximately 1200 pounds per second.

The thrust of the clustered engine of the Saturn is approximately 1.6 million pounds. If its exhaust velocity is also 8000 feet per second, how much propellant does it use per second? It will, of course, be 1.6×10^6 divided by 8000, or 200 slugs per second.

Whereas rocket vehicle designers often use the exhaust velocity as a measure of engine performance, the engine designers more commonly use the related quantity of *specific impulse* or *specific thrust*. The word *specific*, as used in science, means that a certain physical quantity is being designated for a *unit* of *measure* such as mass. Thus *specific heat* refers to the heat content of a unit mass of a material, *specific gravity* refers to the mass of a unit volume. Likewise, *specific impulse* refers to the impulse of a unit mass, and *specific thrust* refers to the thrust of a unit of mass flow rate.

The physical quantity called *impulse* is the product of force and time and is equal to momentum. Thus, $F = mv/t$ and $Ft = mv$. The impulse delivered by a rocket engine during the time interval t is the product of t and the rocket thrust. If t is equal to the total burning time of the rocket, we have the *total impulse, Tt*. Now the specific impulse can be found by simply dividing the total impulse by the mass, m, of propellant. Thus specific impulse, I_{sp}, is equal to Tt/m.

If the thrust of a rocket is 10,000 pounds, the burning time is one second and the mass of propellant is one slug, we see that the specific impulse of the rocket is 10,000 feet per second and we find that specific impulse is exactly equivalent to exhaust velocity.

Now what about specific thrust? In this case it is required to find the thrust per unit of mass flow rate. Thus we divide T by $\dot{m}$ to get $T/\dot{m}$ or $T/m/t$, which is equal to Tt/m. This is apparently the same quantity as specific impulse and therefore is equal to exhaust velocity. In fact we can easily prove this by writing $Tt/m = c$ and rearranging back to the original form of Newton's second law—$T = mc/t$. Note once more that this equation only holds for consistent sets of units, and if we want the thrust to be in pounds the mass must be in slugs!

However, suppose out of sheer cussedness we insist on expressing both force (thrust) and mass in pounds. Then what happens? Actually we must confess that rocket engineers often do exactly that. In fact, that is the normal state of affairs!

If mass is expressed in pounds instead of slugs, the numerical value of the quantity of matter measured will be increased by a factor of 32.2. Thus m (number of pounds) $= 32.2m$ (number of slugs). Now note carefully that the physical dimension on both sides of this equation is mass; we are simply changing units, and 32.2 is a dimensionless conversion factor. Do not make the mistake of assuming that this is the quantity acceleration, with the dimensions of distance divided by time squared. If so, we would be multiplying mass times acceleration, and the quantity on the left would be force!

Since

$$T \text{ (pounds)} = \frac{m \text{ (slugs)} c}{t}$$

then

$$T \text{ (pounds)} = \frac{m \text{ (pounds)} c}{32.2t}$$

which is often written

$$T = \frac{mc}{gt}$$

Rearranging this to the form defining specific impulse results in

$$\frac{Tt}{m} = \frac{c}{g}$$

The units of the left side of the equation are now pound (force) seconds per pound (mass) and the units on the right must be equivalent. In Chapter 3 it was suggested that one pound (force) second per pound (mass) be called a stapp, where one stapp equals 32.2 feet per second. It should not be necessary at this point to remind the reader that the strange process of cancelling pounds-mass against pounds-force to express specific impulse in seconds is both incorrect and misleading. Specific impulse is a measure of velocity, not of time!

As a final check on the accuracy of this statement, try a simple dimensional analysis of the quantity Tt/M or Ft/m. From the second law we know that $m = F/a$; thus

$$\frac{Ft}{m} = \frac{Ft}{F/a} = ta$$

But a equals v/t; thus

$$ta = v \quad \text{and} \quad \frac{Ft}{m} = v$$

The relation between exhaust velocity in feet per second and specific impulse in pound (force) seconds per pound (mass) (or stapps) is then simply the dimensionless quantity 32.2. The vacuum specific impulse of lox plus kerosene is then 310 stapps ($c = 10,000$ feet per second). The vacuum I_{sp} of lox plus liquid hydrogen is about 420 stapps ($c = 13,500$ feet per second).

CHEMICAL ROCKETS

Chemical rockets include all devices which derive their propulsive energy from the chemical energy of their propellants which are carried within the rocket and which provide reaction mass as well as energy. The propellants can be liquid, solid or gas and can involve one or more chemical entities. Thus there are monopropellants, bipropellants and even tripropellants. Almost any two chemicals which will react together and release energy could be used as the components of a bipropellant rocket, but unless carefully selected the rocket would have poor performance. In order to build rockets capable of orbital and escape velocity, it is necessary to select the most energetic combinations of chemicals.

Those familiar with the periodic table of the chemical elements know that the most energetic of the electro-positive elements are hydrogen and the alkali metals of Group I. These are lithium, sodium, potassium, rubidium and cesium. As we proceed down this list, the atomic weight increases as we add protons and neutrons to the nucleus of the atom. The most electro-positive element in the group is cesium, since it has the greatest number of protons in its nucleus. The most active negative elements are the Halogen family at the right side of the table—Group VIII.

From this quick glance at some possible propellants, it appears that cesium and iodine would give the greatest energy release which would be true if we were looking for the most energy *per molecule*. However, for the most energy *per pound* we should use hydrogen and fluorine. The idea is to minimize the number of neutrons in the propellant atoms since they contribute nothing to the chemical energy of the reaction.

Unfortunately, fluorine has ten neutrons and there is no highly negative element with less than this number. If only there were a negative element with the charge-to-mass ratio of hydrogen, there would be no need for nuclear rockets. A simple chemical engine using this combination could develop about 1500 stapps specific impulse. Perhaps some day we will be able to manufacture a synthetic element with these desirable properties.

A liquid chemical propulsion system includes several standard components. There is the engine proper in which the propellants are mixed and burned. The engine includes the combustion chamber, the injector plate (something like an ordinary bathroom shower head) and the nozzle. Modern rocket engines are normally regeneratively cooled to avoid overheating and melting of the engine walls. This cooling process is done by making the engine wall double and circulating one of the propellants between the walls before injecting it into the engine.

Propellants are transferred to the engine from the propellant storage tanks (sometimes considered part of the propulsion system and sometimes a separate part of the vehicle) by high-speed turbo-pumps. Engineers often express concern over the additional complexity and consequent reduction in reliability brought about by the inclusion of these very high-performance subsystems along with their required separate power supplies, controls, etc. Some believe that we should go to the simpler, but lower performance pressurized tank system in which the propellants are forced directly into the engine by high gas pressure in the storage tank. However, this method of propellant feed requires stronger and heavier tanks with consequent reduction in over-all performance.

It may be that rockets will someday be built that are so large that the hydrostatic pressure in the tanks will be sufficient to force the propellants against the high combustion pressure in the engine. A rocket would have to be close to one thousand feet high to use a hydrostatic propellant feed to an engine operating at 500 pounds per square inch. Sizes of this magnitude are not likely in the immediate future.

Solid propellants employ a semi-plastic mixture of fuel and oxidizer cast directly into an expendable tank that serves as a combined storage vessel, rocket structure and combination chamber. The solid mixture is called the *grain*.

It is possible to make a solid propellant from a high-energy, solid oxidizer and almost any solid, combustible material. Ordinary gun powder was used in early rockets and is sometimes still used by amateurs in spite of the obvious hazards. Gun powder is a mixture of the fuels charcoal (carbon) and sulfur, with the oxidizer, potassium nitrate—KNO_3.

Another dangerous mixture often used by ill-advised amateurs is zinc and sulfur. Note that in this case sulfur is the oxidizer. It should be understood that an oxidizer or an oxidizing agent is one that acts like oxygen in a chemical reaction—it need not contain oxygen. It is an electro-negative element or compound which contributes electrons to a chemical reaction. The Halogen family of electro-negative elements discussed above are good examples.

Other materials that have been used as solid fuels are rubber, tar and paraffin wax. These are hydrocarbon fuels related in composition to the liquid fuel—kerosene. Other plastic and rubber-like solids are also used. One in common use today is called *polyurethane*. This is sometimes combined with aluminum powder to add energy to the reaction. Some solid oxidizers, in addition to potassium nitrate, are potassium chlorate and potassium- lithium-, or ammonium perchlorate.

The fuel component of the solid propellant is usually called upon to supply the mechanical properties needed for a practical, safe and reliable rocket since the oxidizers are generally brittle, crystalline materials. One of the greatest causes of catastrophic failure in solid rockets in the past has been the occasional development of cracks in the grain during expansion or contraction resulting from temperature change or during solidification from the liquid "melt."

A crack in a solid propellant grain is a serious matter, since a larger than intended burning surface may thus be exposed. This results in more rapid burning, faster production of combustion gases, increase in temperature and pressure beyond the chain reaction point where the whole mass of propellant will react and, finally, detonation. Obviously, great care must be exercised in development, production, loading and handling of solid rockets to prevent development of such hazardous conditions.

CHAPTER 15

Advanced Propulsion Systems

D
EVELOPMENT OF NUCLEAR rockets for space flight is already underway, and revolutionary advances in capability can be expected. However, we should not expect as great a jump in performance in advancing from chemical to nuclear rockets as was realized in the giant step from chemical to nuclear bombs. Although the energy is available for truly great advances in performance, we have not learned how to handle it yet and must be content with relatively modest increases in the immediate future.

NUCLEAR REACTOR ROCKETS

Problems arise in transferring heat energy from the nuclear reactor to the inert expellant material—usually liquid hydrogen. The heat must be transferred through the solid walls of the nuclear reactor in order to heat the hydrogen to the required high temperatures. This limits the working temperature of the hydrogen to something less than the melting point of the reactor walls. Since the solid walls are held together by chemical forces, we have not actually been able to get beyond chemical energy limitations, even in the nuclear rocket! We cannot operate at any higher temperature in a nuclear rocket than in a chemical rocket!

Since this is the case, one might wonder why the nuclear rocket offers any advantage at all. This goes back to our discussion in Chapter 14 of the desirability of a low atomic weight oxidizer containing no neutrons. In the nuclear rocket we need no oxidizer and can use pure hydrogen for expellant material. This is the only advantage in these early applications of nuclear energy to rocketry, and for this we must pay the price of a heavy reactor and the hazards associated with its use.

Nevertheless, the Rover-type nuclear rocket represents a very important step forward and considerable improvement in space travel capability. Upper stage applications of the Rover or Nerva engine should have vacuum specific impulse values of 1000 to 1200 stapps. The higher figure is approximately three times the value for hydrogen-oxygen rockets. If everything else is equal, this means a velocity change capability three times as great.

Suppose that a chemical second stage of a rocket is boosted to velocity of 8000 feet per second and can, itself, generate a velocity change of 18,000 feet per second and thus carry its payload into orbit. If we now substitute a nuclear second stage of equal weight with an equal payload, it could carry this pay-

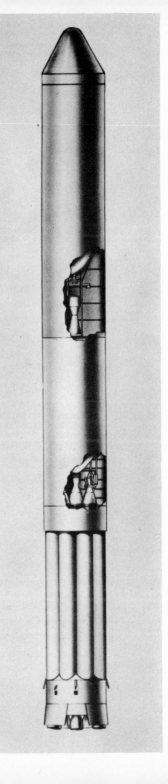

Fig. 15-1 Saturn booster with nuclear upper stage.

Illus.: Courtesy NASA

load through a velocity change of 62,000 feet per second. Since this is more than enough for round-trip interplanetary flights, the significance of the advance to nuclear rockets should be clear. Whereas chemical rockets will carry us to orbit and, at considerable cost, to the moon, nuclear rockets will carry us to the planets!

ELECTRIC ROCKETS

Exhaust velocities of thermodynamic chemical and nuclear rockets are limited by the temperatures which can be sustained in the rocket engines. Because of these limitations scientists long ago began to speculate on other means of accelerating reaction mass. Physicists were familiar with other methods of exerting accelerating forces on matter, and electrostatic forces looked particularly interesting to Oberth and later students of space travel.

In this age of atom-smashing machines it is well-known that charged atoms or *ions* can be accelerated to a very high speed by electrostatic or electromagnetic fields. If we could carry one of these particle accelerators on a space ship along with a source of electric power, we could use it as a means of propulsion. Actually this can be done, but the first calculations made of performance are apt to be disappointing. Because of the very large mass associated with the power supply (probably a nuclear reactor plus electric-generating equipment) and the particle accelerator and the relatively small mass of ions ejected per second, the thrust-to-weight ratio of the ion-propelled vehicle is extremely low. The first practical vehicles of this type will have acceleration capabilities of no better than about 10^{-5} gee or 0.000322 feet per second. Although apparently insignificant, even such low values as this would be valuable for course corrections and orientations of orbiting space ships.

When electric propulsion systems can be improved to the point that constant accelerations on the order of 10^{-4} gee can be sustained, they become of interest for flights to Mars, Venus and the more distant planets. Flight time to Mars at this acceleration is approximately nine months. This is a competitive trip time to a minimum energy trip by chemical or nuclear (thermal) rocket and much more efficient in terms of payload. Because of this high specific impulse of the electric rocket (several thousand stapps), the payload can be from one-fifth to one-third of the total vehicle mass.

Even higher accelerations may be possible with future, constant acceleration systems. Figure 15-2 shows travel times for such systems with constant accelerations of 10^{-4} gee or better. If an electric system could be developed which could sustain a constant acceleration of 10^{-2} gee, it would take only three weeks for a trip to Mars and six weeks for a trip to Jupiter. In another ten years we may be thinking seriously about building such vehicles.

Actually, ion rockets may not be the best approach to the high I_{sp}, 10^{-2} gee system. Plasma, arc and colloid rockets also under study or development in many laboratories may offer better hope for the high performance required for short-time flights to the planets.

In an ion rocket, charged atoms are expelled from the vehicle by strong electrostatic or electromagnetic fields. In order to balance the charge of the ship, both positive and negative particles must be repelled in two separate exhaust streams. A plasma rocket also expels charged particles, but in this case both the positive and negative ions are mixed together in the same exhaust stream. A plasma is an ionized yet neutral gas.

When the temperature of a solid is raised, it eventually reaches its melting point and changes to the liquid phase. If we continue to add energy to the material, it will reach its boiling point and then change to the third state of matter, the gaseous phase. When considerably more energy is added and the temperature of the gas is raised to several thousand degrees, it begins to change into the fourth state of matter—the plasma phase—in which the molecules begin to dissociate into atoms and the atoms lose or gain electrons to become ions. When this happens the gas becomes a good conductor of electricity. If it is then exposed to a changing magnetic field, it will be set in motion just as the metallic, conducting armature of an electric motor. Thus a plasma can be accelerated

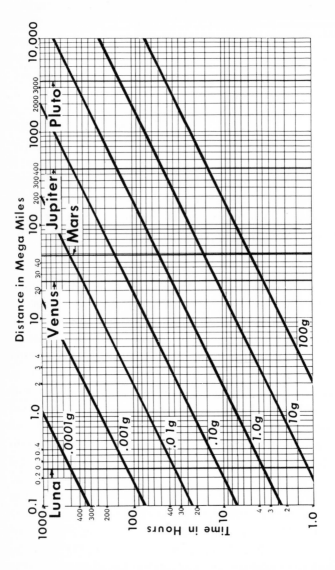

Fig. 15-2 Time for constant acceleration interplanetary trips with midpoint turnaround.

to a very high speed by a magnetic field and fired from the rear of a space vehicle. A plasma rocket has a somewhat higher thrust-to-weight ratio than an ion rocket but a lower specific impulse.

The colloid rocket is similar to the ion rocket but, again, has lower specific impulse and higher acceleration capability. In this system charged oil droplets are repelled from the space vehicle by electrostatic fields. Accelerations of 10^{-3} gee are considered attainable at I_{sp} values of approximately 2000 stapps.

The arc rocket represents still another method of converting energy (solar or nuclear) into kinetic energy of reaction mass, which has the advantage of a low molecular weight working fluid (hydrogen) yet no problem of heat transfer through solid walls as in the nuclear rocket. This would seem to be an ideal way to use nuclear energy. Unfortunately, the equipment necessary to convert from nuclear to electrical energy is so massive that the thrust-to-weight ratio is of the same order as the ion and plasma rockets.

Still another technique employing wires which are exploded by high-density electric currents suffers from the same disadvantage of high hardware mass and resulting low thrust-to-weight ratio.

When men fly to Mars and Venus they will probably wish to reduce flight time by converting nuclear energy to kinetic energy as rapidly as possible in high-thrust systems. Thus the direct Rover (solid reactor) thermal method will be used rather than the ion, plasma, arc, colloid, etc., indirect conversion methods. However, for instruments or freight, time of flight may not be so important as maximizing payload, and the low-thrust systems will find useful application. When constant-thrust systems can develop continuous accelerations of 10^{-2} gees or better, as they probably will within 20 years, they may become competitive for manned interplanetary flights.

AIR-BREATHING ENGINES

Many books on astronautics ignore air-breathing engines completely. It is often argued that air-breathers cannot operate in a vacuum and therefore are not important to space travel. This is a serious misconception. We would be much closer to economical space travel today if advanced air-breathing engines had received more support in the late 1950's. Unfortunately, research on advanced air-breathers was cut off almost completely in favor of rocket research during this period.

Air-breathing engines *are* important to space travel because a vehicle must travel through the atmosphere before it gets into space. The most difficult part of space travel is just getting there. It is much easier to go from a close earth orbit to the moon, than to go from the earth's surface to orbit.

It is obviously inefficient to carry oxidizer and reaction mass along in a rocket in order to propel the rocket through a rich oxidizing medium. However, there have been difficult problems to overcome in designing air-breathing engines which could compete with the basically simple rocket engine on an over-all basis. These problems have generally been connected with the high temperatures generated by high-speed travel through the air and the handling of air of varying pressure, density, temperature and flow speed in a single engine of fixed geometry.

There are now encouraging signs that these problems will be solved and that air-breathing engines will play a major part in the conquest of space.

Turbojet engines have often been proposed for first-stage boosters for space vehicles. Their primary advantage over rocket engines is in fuel economy which can be expressed in specific impulse. The fuel specific impulse for turbojets can be several thousand stapps for both liquid hydrogen and hydrocarbon fuels. The thrust-to-weight ratio of turbojet engines is high compared to rockets of comparable I_{sp} (the electric rockets) but is low compared to chemical rockets. It is on the order of ten as compared to about 100 for rockets. Also the cost of turbojets is high and the development time is longer than for the rocket engine. Because of high engine costs, turbojet boosters would have to be recoverable.

Experimental turbojet engines have run at Mach 3 and it is generally acknowledged that they will soon go to Mach 4. It may be that they will eventually go even faster if not replaced by superior systems. A fully recoverable and reusable turbojet booster capable of attaining speeds from Mach 4 to Mach 6 could bring a tremendous reduction in space travel transportation costs compared to current chemical rocket systems.

The ramjet is simpler than the turbojet and less expensive. It also has a high thrust-to-weight ratio mid-way between that of the turbojet and rockets. It has a fuel specific impulse of several thousand stapps and can operate at speeds of Mach 6 and higher. Some recent design studies indicate a possibility of efficient ramjet operation all the way to orbital speed (26,000 feet per second) or even escape speed (37,000 feet per second). Of course it would be necessary for the space vehicle to remain in the upper atmosphere until reaching its maximum velocity, after which it could coast all the way to the moon.

Ramjets have the disadvantage that they must be boosted to high speed before they can operate. They have zero static thrust. Also they have had very poor variable speed capability. They could develop high thrust and specific impulse at design speed, but both quantities would fall off very rapidly above and below this speed. Considerable improvement is now in sight and the ramjet has real promise as a component of air-breathing space boosters.

Obviously it would be desirable if we could somehow make use of nuclear energy in a ramjet. In fact such a system would seem to be ideal—close to the ultimate in efficiency. The fuel specific impulse of such vehicles would, theoretically, be enormously high since only a small amount of nuclear fuel would be needed.

Actually, such devices are already under development. Nuclear ramjet engines have already been tested under Project Pluto. However, there are no immediate prospects for application to space booster systems since present nuclear ramjets are severely speed-limited. They can operate efficiently only in a narrow speed range near Mach 3. Below their design speed they will not have sufficient air flow to maintain thrust. Above Mach 3 their nuclear reactors would soon be destroyed by high-temperature heat loads.

The problem is somewhat similar to that of the nuclear rocket in that heat must be transferred from the reactor through a solid wall to the working fluid. The difficulty is more pronounced in the case of the ramjet, however, because the working fluid is an oxidizer. Most reactor materials would quickly burn up when exposed to air at the high operating temperatures of the nuclear ramjet.

The Pluto system employs reactor elements imbedded in beryllia (beryllium oxide) which stands up to these extreme conditions better than any other material that has been tried. Even so, tests show that the Pluto reactor will burn out after only a few hours of operation. Thus the whole weight of the reactor must be considered expendable fuel. The specific impulse, although very high, is a long way from the theoretical condition in which only a small amount of uranium would be "burned."

Two of the most exciting propulsion developments in recent years are an air-breathing engine called *LACE*, for Liquid Air Cycle Engine, and a nuclear version of LACE called *NULACE*. Until early 1961 practically all information on LACE was classified and the public was not aware of its existence. However, in May 1961 Congress released enough information to give a general picture of how this revolutionary new system will operate.

Basically, LACE is a bipropellant rocket engine burning liquid hydrogen and liquid air or liquid oxygen. Although classed as an air-breather, it operates on liquid propellants and uses turbopumps and a rocket combustion chamber. The enormous heat capacity of the liquid hydrogen is used to liquefy the air which enters through an intake in the front of the vehicle, passes through a heat exchanger and is then conducted in liquid form to the turbopump. LACE has a very high specific impulse, high static thrust and a thrust-to-weight ratio approaching that of a rocket. For these reasons alone it would be highly competitive with turbojets and ramjets. However, it has another striking advantage. The air, once liquefied, need not be consumed immediately but may be stored for future use. As air density decreases with altitude and air-breathing engine efficiency declines, some of the stored air can be added to the oxidizer-fuel mixture. Eventually, when the vehicle leaves the atmosphere, LACE operates as a pure hydrogen-oxygen rocket.

It often appears advantageous to combine or "marry" two or more propulsion systems with the intention of producing a superior system with the advantages of both. However, the usual result is a "bastard" mixture with only mediocre performance and much greater complexity. Sometimes, as in the hybrid, solid-liquid rocket or the air turborocket, the compromise may appear to have considerable usefulness even though no striking gains in performance can be expected.

In the combination of the LACE system with the Rover nuclear rocket, NULACE, it appears possible that the performance could actually be the sum of the two engine performances rather than the usual disappointing average. The heat energy supplied to the hydrogen by the burning of the hydrogen in liquid oxygen (obtained from the air) could be added to the energy already supplied by the Rover nuclear reactor. Thus specific impulse would be higher than for either LACE or Rover. The Marquardt Company, developers of both LACE and NULACE, say that the specific impulse of NULACE would be more than twice that of Rover. Thus we could expect something between 1500 and 2000 stapps.

NULACE might be considered to have three propulsion modes: pure LACE for take-off and acceleration to supersonic speeds, mixed LACE and Rover operation after attaining sufficient altitude to eliminate any danger from the nuclear engine and, finally, pure Rover operation after leaving the atmosphere and exhausting any stored oxygen that had been carried into space.

It might be necessary to shut off the engine temporarily after phase one. Then a valve would be opened between the combustion chamber and the reactor, liquid hydrogen would be diverted through the reactor and hot gaseous hydrogen would begin to flow from the reactor to the combustion chamber where liquid oxygen would be added to the hydrogen. After propellant flows had been increased to the full operating levels, NULACE would be running at its peak performance, combining nuclear and chemical heating of its exhaust gas. This super performance would continue as long as the oxygen supply lasted. If hydrogen still remained then, pure Rover operation could be continued.

No details have been made public as to the optimum proportions of liquid hydrogen and liquid oxygen to carry beyond the atmosphere, but it would obviously be advisable to depart, from the highest feasible altitude and velocity at which the air storage operation could take place, with fully loaded propellant tanks. With the possible exception of the nuclear pulse rocket, no system within the reach of present-day engineering appears so promising.

NUCLEAR PULSE ROCKETS

Although modern hydrogen bombs are still extremely inefficient compared to the fusion energy theoretically obtainable, they nevertheless represent an increase in available energy per pound to the order of one million times the highest energy chemicals. In view of this it may be difficult to understand why the exhaust energy of a Rover nuclear rocket is only about four times that of a chemical rocket (approximately twice the exhaust velocity). As explained in the section on nuclear reactor rockets, this relatively low performance is due to the limiting, chemical-energy bonds holding together the solid walls of the nuclear reactor. Above a certain limiting temperature these chemical forces are no longer strong enough to preserve the integrity of the walls—that is, they melt. Thus the nuclear rocket is limited by the strength of chemical forces whereas the nuclear bomb is not.

Even the chemical rocket is not so temperature limited as the nuclear rocket, since the chemical energy is released inside the rocket thrust chamber at some distance from the walls. If necessary, the walls can be cooled by *film cooling,* in which a layer of fuel is directed along the wall surface, or by transpiration cooling, wherein the fuel is forced directly through a porous thrust chamber wall. Such cooling methods cannot be used in the nuclear rocket since the heat must flow through the solid wall of the reactor in order to raise the temperature of the working fluid.

In the nuclear pulse rocket this limitation is avoided, since the energy is released in the working fluid at considerable distance from the solid parts of the rocket.

There are two principal types of nuclear pulse rockets, known as Orion, and CONEX, both depending on the use of small nuclear bombs for propulsion. In Orion the explosions occur behind the vehicle, and in CONEX they occur inside a more conventional thrust chamber (Contained Explosion).

Fig. 15-3 Schematic diagram of Contained Explosion Nuclear Pulse Rocket (CONEX).

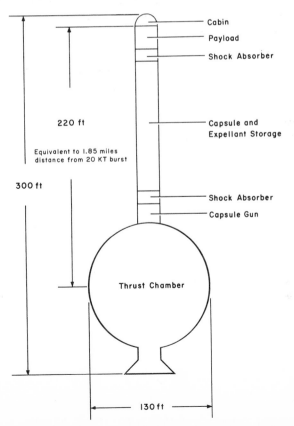

The Orion project was severely limited by the ban on nuclear explosions, but several million dollars have been spent on theoretical and laboratory studies. The program is highly classified and results have not been made public.

In the Orion design small atomic bombs are exploded at some distance behind the vehicle, and the vehicle is impelled forward by the force of the explosion wave striking its rear surface. The process is obviously very inefficient in terms of energy utilization, but the energy release is so great that performance several times that of the reactor rockets is considered possible.

The CONEX design is more efficient than Orion in utilizing the energy released by the bomb since the bomb is set off inside a thrust chamber. However, it has to contend with problems of very high pressure and temperature and resulting high thrust chamber weight. It is generally considered that CONEX represents a more difficult development problem than Orion, but that it also offers potentially higher performance and greater economy.

Specific impulses of several thousand seconds should be possible with either Orion or CONEX at high thrust-to-weight levels, permitting manned travel to any part of the solar system.

CHAPTER 16

Elementary Space Vehicle Design

Now that the velocity and energy requirements of several important missions have been considered (Chapter 7) and the capabilities of various propulsion systems have also been surveyed, it is possible to proceed to the design of vehicles which can transport our desired payloads to destinations in space.

Obviously, the reader cannot expect to become an expert space vehicle designer simply by reading this book. The material presented here will permit only a "first cut" or conceptual design that will be no better than the designer's experience, judgment and selection of input values. Accurate, detailed designs require the use of complex procedures and mathematical techniques which will not be discussed here.

However, the conceptual vehicles which can be designed with the simple methods given here should not be disparaged. They can be very useful in advance planning studies, comparative evaluations of different proposed designs, cost estimates, etc. Also, the accuracy of the performance estimates derived in this fashion are often surpassed only by the experimental results of the actual flight tests. Modifications found to be necessary during the test program can easily change the final performance of the vehicle by a factor as large as the inaccuracy of these first-approximation methods.

In approaching the problem of a first-approximation design, we first divide the vehicle into three basic parts: the structure, the propellant and the payload. These three parts together make up the total mass, or gross mass, of the vehicle at take-off.

The vehicle structure, S, includes the engines, propellant tanks, connecting and supporting members, guidance, controls, auxiliary power, etc. Guidance is sometimes considered part of the payload and there is no harm in this as long as it is clearly indicated as such. It is only when a part gets lost and is not included in either category that trouble arises.

The payload, L, includes everything we wish to carry to our destination plus the enclosing capsule. The latter item, although customarily considered payload for rocket vehicles, is normally included as structure in conventional transportation systems. Again, it is a matter of keeping the books straight and not putting the debits in the credits column!

The propellant mass, P, should include only what is actually used for propulsion. As much as two or three per cent of the total propellant mass is sometimes left in the vehicle at burn-out, when either fuel or oxidizer is used up too quickly and the remaining propellant cannot be consumed. Thus this "outage" must be counted as "structure" rather than useful propellant.

DESIGN EQUATIONS

An even simpler approach to design estimates than that outlined above involves dividing the vehicle into only two parts rather than three. These are *dead mass,* or *empty mass, E,* and *propellant mass, P.* Obviously, E plus P equals the *gross mass* or *take-off mass, G.* Also, from the previous discussion, $E = S + L$.

Now, if the mission velocity is called v, and the exhaust velocity is written c, we can write the basic space vehicle design equation:

$$v = c \ln \frac{G}{E}$$

where ln stands for natural logarithm.

Those familiar with natural logarithms know that this equation can be rewritten as

$$e^{v/c} = \frac{G}{E}$$

after first dividing both sides by c to obtain

$$\frac{v}{c} = \ln \frac{G}{E}$$

Actually, the relation between the last two forms of the equation defines what is meant by the natural logarithm of a number (the number is G/E in this case) which is "the power to which e must be raised to give the number." The power to which e must be raised is, of course, v/c; therefore, this is equal to $\ln (G/E)$.

It might be useful to further emphasize the importance of this relation and fix it more firmly in the reader's memory by calling it "the first law of rocketry" and stating it in words as follows: *The velocity ratio of a rocket is equal to the natural logarithm of the mass ratio.*

This first law of rocket flight obviously can be used for a first crude estimate of a rocket vehicle design. If we know what empty mass, E, is desired at a mission velocity, v, we can choose a propellant combination with an exhaust velocity, c, and proceed to calculate the take-off mass, G, of the rocket. If desired, the propellant mass, P, can be found by subtracting E from G, then the propellant volume can be found by dividing the mass by the density.

There is one obvious defect in this procedure—we have not found the payload mass. It is really not too interesting to find the dead mass unless we also can find out what part of it is structure and what part is payload.

One approach to this problem would be to go through the analysis above, starting with an arbitrary value of E, and find the corresponding value of G. At this point we would have to make an estimate of what fraction of E could reasonably be payload and still leave sufficient structure for a vehicle of mass, G. More systematically, we might assume a payload, L, and subtract this from the take-off mass to find the booster mass, $G - L$. Then, by consulting data on current rocket designs, we would determine the reasonable fraction of this that could be propellant. Following this procedure, the propellant fraction, F, can be defined as $P/(G - L)$: This tells us how much of the booster mass is structure and how much is propellant.

Following this procedure, we could eventually arrive at some consistent values after several trials. However, it is much easier to use a systematic approach from the beginning. We can take one equation containing the five quantities of interest and, providing that four are known, solve for the fifth quantity. This equation, which might be called the rocket conceptual design equation, is

$$\frac{G}{L} = \frac{F}{e^{-v/c} + F - 1}$$

which is really nothing more than a rearrangement of the first law of rocket flight. The derivation is quite easy when you know how to do it, but you might enjoy trying it on your own before consulting the method used in Appendix I.

Now it is time to design a rocket. Suppose that we have a payload of 10,000 pounds on the moon that we want to propel back to earth. A minimum velocity of about 7800 feet per second is required to escape from the moon and the atmosphere can be used to slow the vehicle down as it approaches the earth. However, there will be some gravity loss in escaping from the moon, and some extra capability should be included for steering and emergencies. A good round number to use is 10,000 feet per second. This happens to be very convenient because the vacuum exhaust velocity for liquid oxygen and kerosene is also approximately 10,000. Thus v and c are equal and $v/c = 1$. Then

$$e^{-v/c} = e^{-1} = \frac{1}{2.72}$$

which is 0.368.

The hardest decision to make is what number to assume for the propellant, fraction F, since it depends on what type of re-entry body is to be used (this might be charged against the payload), how much radiation shielding, etc. Also, it depends on the size of the vehicle, since the larger the vehicle the less important are such constant-weight items as guidance, etc.

Assuming that guidance, shielding, power supplies, etc., are included in the 10,000 pounds of payload, it should be possible to achieve a propellant fraction of about 0.85 or even 0.90. If we are optimistic and use 0.90,

$$\frac{G}{L} = \frac{0.90}{0.368 + 0.90 - 1.0} = \frac{0.90}{0.268} = 3.36$$

If the more conservative value of 0.85 were assumed, then G/L would equal

$$\frac{0.85}{0.215} = 3.94 \quad \text{or} \quad G = 40,000 \text{ pounds}$$

Now suppose that liquid hydrogen and liquid oxygen could be used for the moon-to-earth rocket. For this combination it is reasonable to assume a vacuum exhaust velocity of 13,500 feet per second. Therefore, $v/c = 0.74$. Because of the low density of liquid hydrogen, the propellant fraction must be decreased to 0.80 to 0.85. Perhaps there will be no over-all gain in performance. Now

$$\frac{G}{L} = \frac{0.80}{e^{-0.74} - 0.20} = \frac{0.80}{0.477 - 0.20}$$

$$= \frac{0.80}{0.277} = 2.9$$

Thus the vehicle will now weigh only 29,000 pounds in spite of the decrease in propellant fraction. (For values of the powers of e, consult Appendix II.)

It might seem odd to start with a moon-earth vehicle in designing a moon rocket, but that is actually a good place to begin. In fact, an even better place to start is with the re-entry vehicle. However, we skipped that phase and merely assumed that it would weigh 10,000 pounds. Now we know that it will be necessary to land 30,000 to 40,000 pounds on the moon in order to return 10,000 pounds to earth. But how much must be carried to escape velocity in order to land 30,000 to 40,000 pounds on the moon?

Again the minimum velocity change required is 7800 feet per second, and 10,000 feet per second should provide a reasonable allowance for landing maneuvers. Then, if the same propellants and propellant fractions are assumed, the gross-to-payload ratios will again be about three or four to one. Thus the payload carried to escape velocity is from 90,000 to 160,000 pounds, depending on the choice of propellants.

Now the transition from orbital velocity, 26,000 feet per second, to escape velocity, 37,000 feet per second, would require about 11,000 feet per second, if the orbit was at sea level. Actually, the velocity of escape from a 300-mile orbit is only 35,000 feet per second. Again, a round number of 10,000 feet per second is a fair approximation, and the multiplying figure is about three to four. In fact, this is a bit conservative since the vehicle is quite large and higher propellant fractions could be assumed. However, using $G/L = 3$ or 4, the payload boosted from orbit now becomes 270,000 to 640,000 pounds. Note that what started out as only a 30% difference in mass is now over 100%!

The really big part of the job of space flight is the first part—boosting vehicles into orbit. That takes an ideal velocity change of about 26,000 feet per second. However, because of gravity loss and drag loss, almost entirely during first-stage burning, we should allow about 30,000 feet per second. The earth-to-orbit booster may use three stages, and a reasonable division of velocity is 10,000 feet per second per stage. In practice, the first stage will achieve only about 6000 feet per second out of its allotted 10,000 feet per second.

If we use a multiplying factor of three for each stage, the total G/L for the orbital vehicle is 27. If four for each stage, it is 64. Thus the take-off weight for the vehicle might be anywhere from 7.3×10^6 pounds to 41×10^6 pounds.

The smaller estimate is actually quite close to the gross mass of the Saturn C–5, which is being developed for the lunar landing mission. Saturn C–5 has a thrust of 7.5×10^6 pounds and a gross mass of about 5×10^6 pounds. Liquid hydrogen is used in upper stages, as in our example.

The question of division of velocity between stages was glossed over rather quickly in the foregoing example. Actually, it can be proved that, for ideal conditions and equally efficient stages (propellant fractions and exhaust velocities equal), stage burn-out velocities should be equal to give the highest total velocity change. A reasonable rule of thumb is to use the same mass multiplying factor (gross-to-payload ratio) for all stages, regardless of efficiency, thus giving a greater fraction of the total velocity change to the higher performance stages. More refined calculations show that even more mass should be concentrated in the high-performance stages, but either the equal velocity or equal gross-to-payload ratio is satisfactory for the first-approximation design. Over-all performance can be improved by trial and error changes in staging if desired, but extensive optimization will give only illusory improvements without detailed consideration of drag and gravity losses.

The space vehicle design equation has been plotted on Figs. 16-1 and 16-2 for payload ratios, G/L, up to 14 to one. The other two basic design quantities plotted are the velocity ratio, v/c, and the propellant ratio or propellant fraction, F.

It should be noted that the most efficient and economical designs are those in the maximum curvature areas, the "knees" of the curves. As shown, these combinations give the maximum payload kinetic energy. They also are the areas of maximum sensitivity of one function to the other. As the design point moves out on the arms of the curve in either direction, large changes in one function are required to produce small changes in the others.

Thus the payload ratio should ideally be somewhere in the range from two to five. When it becomes larger than this, it is usually desirable to stage the rocket to reduce the payload ratio for each stage. Thus the payload ratio in the example above was held down between 2.5 and four per stage.

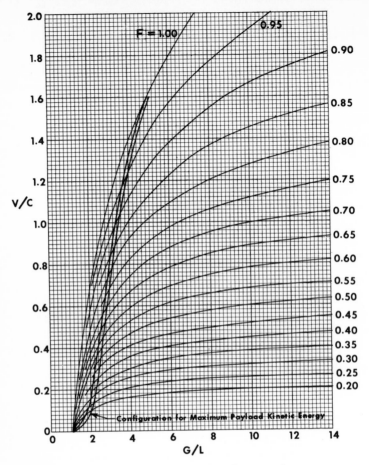

Fig. 16-1 Rocket vehicle design aid.

After preliminary sizing of the rocket with a first-approximation division of mass between stages, it is desirable to estimate the thrust required per stage. This will then permit the important next step of selecting the engines which will propel our conceptual space vehicle. Since the engines have the longest development time of any of the rocket components, this is the most important design decision we will make.

There is no hard and fast rule about the relation between thrust and weight for our vehicle except that first-stage thrust must obviously exceed the total, or take-off, weight if the launch is to be vertical. Thus we can say $T/G > 1$ is a requirement for vertical take-off, but it is difficult to go beyond this in any general way.

Ideally, the thrust-to-weight ratio should be infinite for vertical launch if drag, engine cost and other practical problems are ignored. With infinite thrust, burning time is zero and no propellant need be lifted against gravity. Thus gravity loss is zero. In practice it is not desirable to build up speed too rapidly in the lower atmosphere, since drag is roughly proportional to the square of the velocity, and it is generally inadvisable to employ take-off thrusts greater than twice the vehicle gross weight.

Fig. 16-2   Rocket vehicle design aid.

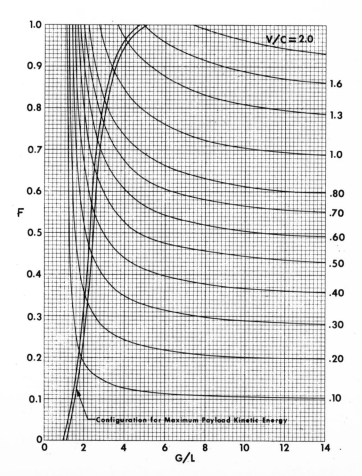

Even more important than drag in limiting thrust-to-weight is the practical problem of engine availability. It is usually desirable to use the latest and most advanced, if not the largest, engine that can be obtained. Once the engine choice has been made, the objective is to boost the largest possible payload with that engine, whether single or clustered.

There is a commonly used design rule of thumb to the effect that the thrust-to-weight ratio should approximate 1.5 to give the highest gross-to-payload ratio. However, after an original design is based on this rule, it is often found that a larger payload can be boosted using the same thrust, if gross weight is increased until $T/G = 1.2$. Since increase in size of propellant tanks and increase in propellant mass add little to the vehicle cost, the cost efficiency can be increased even though the mass efficiency may go down.

A reasonable assumption for second-stage thrust is that it can be approximately equal to the remaining weight of the vehicle. Since gravity loss is reduced by inclining the trajectory toward the horizontal, vertical flight is not ordinarily maintained after leaving the atmosphere. Thus it is no longer necessary for the thrust-to-weight ratio to exceed one.

Thrust-to-weight ratios for upper stages will depend on the mission requirements and may vary from about 10^{-5} gee for electric interplanetary rockets to about 0.25 gee for lunar-landing vehicles. The additional step of determining the vehicle dimensions can rather easily be taken once the stage masses have been found.

The volume of propellants can be found from the formula $V = m/d$, where d is the density of one of the propellants and m its mass. Assuming a cylindrical propellant tank, the dimensions can then be determined from $V = \pi r^2 h$, where h is the height of a right circular cylinder and r is its radius.

CHAPTER 17

Staging
Space Vehicles

IN THE EXAMPLES considered in previous chapters it has been assumed that stages have been arranged in the conventional tandem fashion with the largest stage on the bottom and successively smaller stages stacked above it. However, this tandem arrangement is not the only feasible method. Some advantages might be noted in favor of the lateral or parallel arrangement as well as for various intermediate combinations of tandem and lateral.

Lateral staging can be of two principal types, *simple lateral* and lateral with *cross-pumping* of propellants. In simple lateral staging, stages are clustered side by side, all engines fire simultaneously, and empty stages drop off at one or more staging points leaving the partially filled stages to continue the flight. If the cross-pumping technique is used, the remaining stages are completely loaded with propellants at the staging points. Before staging, all engines have used propellants from the first-stage tanks. After staging, the remaining loaded tanks feed the remaining engines.

As an example of lateral staging, consider a rocket of gross mass equal to one hundred thousand pounds, a propellant fraction of 0.90 and an exhaust velocity of 10,000 feet per second. This rocket, if used singly, could carry 50,000 pounds to 6000 feet per second, ideal velocity. Actually, it might reach only about 3600 feet per second if launched from earth.

Now suppose that four of these rockets were clustered together and were launched with all four engines operating. When half of the total store of propellants had been used up, two of them would be dropped off empty. The remaining two would continue to accelerate. The staging point would be at an ideal velocity of 6000 feet per second. The second pair of rockets might be considered the payload of the first pair.

A second staging point would be reached at 12,000 feet per second after which the remaining rocket would carry its 50,000 pound payload to 18,000 feet per second. Thus a final speed would be attained which was three times the capability of the single rocket for the payload considered.

If the initial rocket had been a cluster of eight instead of four, and four rockets had been discarded at the first staging point, an additional 6000 feet per second could be added to the 18,000 for a total of 24,000 feet per second. Going to a fifth stage—16 rockets with a total mass of 1.6×10^6 pounds—would result in a final velocity of 30,000 feet per second.

Now note that this method of staging is no different in terms of performance than the tandem method using the assumptions of the analysis above. The same staging points, velocities and payloads would have resulted if the 16 rockets had been arranged in tandem rather than parallel or lateral stages. The only difference would be in the engine thrust required. Even this difference would not occur if the whole operation took place in gravity-free space.

The individual engine thrust in the case of tandem staging would have to be twice as great as for the lateral case in order to provide the same thrust-to-weight ratio for earth take-off. This follows, since only eight engines would be operating for tandem as compared to 16 for lateral. Conversely, the highest gross-weight vehicle could be lifted by a given number of engines of some particular thrust range if all engines were arranged in parallel.

As a more specific example, consider that the F–1 engine with 1.5 million pounds of thrust is the largest available in the mid-1960's. Also assume that stages with propellant fractions of 0.95 can be built and that we want to put 500,000 pounds of payload in orbit at minimum vehicle cost. Since the engines are one of the most expensive components of the vehicle, we should minimize the number of engines used.

Assume that individual rocket segments are built with gross mass of one million pounds each and one F–1 engine per segment. If four of these segments were clustered for a first stage of a tandem vehicle, very little weight could be allotted for upper stages. However, if we follow the method used previously and use four segments for the first stage of a lateral vehicle, we could use an additional four segments for subsequent stages. Of the total of eight segments, two would drop off at the second staging point, and one at the third. Each stage would develop a velocity change of 7000 feet per second for a total of 28,000 feet per second. This should be sufficient to carry the payload to low orbit even when losses are subtracted, since a high thrust-to-weight ratio has been assumed and drag losses are low for large vehicles. Each stage should have a payload ratio of two; thus the over-all G/L should equal 16 and L should be 500,000 pounds. An optimally sized, four-stage, tandem vehicle using four F–1's in the first stage could only propel half this payload to the same final velocity. It would also be only half the gross weight, but the cost of tanks and propellants is negligible compared to the engine costs.

If a given number of engines of a specific type and thrust engines are to be used in a space vehicle, higher performance can be attained with lateral than with tandem staging, providing that thrust-to-weight ratio is a major design criterion. However, laterally staged vehicles would be more complex in some respects and thus might be less reliable. However, it should be noted in connection with reliability that all engines will be started on the ground before take-off.

The Atlas vehicle is an example of partial lateral staging in

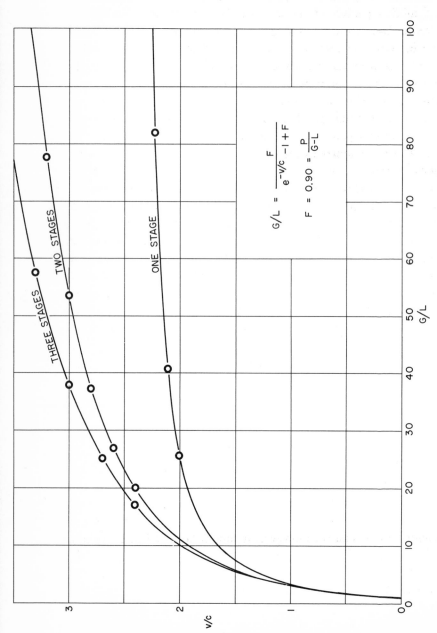

$$\frac{G}{L} = \frac{F}{e^{-v/c} - 1 + F}$$

$$F = 0.90 = \frac{P}{G-L}$$

Fig. 17-1   Effects of velocity ratio and staging on the payload ratio.

which only engines are dropped at the staging point. A single pair of tanks travels all the way to burn-out of the sustainer engine.

Atlas and Titan both use three engines—two with 150,000 pounds thrust and one (sustainer) of 60,000 pounds thrust. Titan has a take-off thrust of 300,000 pounds and Atlas has 360,000 pounds. Atlas can equal the payload performance of Titan in spite of the fact that less mass is discarded at the staging point, primarily because the higher take-off thrust permits Atlas to carry more propellants than Titan in that its thrust is higher. However, the performance of Atlas does not exceed that of Titan because of the incomplete staging. If Atlas were a complete laterally staged vehicle, its payload could exceed that of Titan by the same percentage that its take-off thrust and gross mass exceed those of Titan, that is, by 20%.

Whatever the type employed, staging is a useful substitute for low velocity ratios and high propellant fractions. Whenever the combination of these two ratios is such that the payload ratio exceeds ten, some kind of staging should be seriously considered. In contrast, if G/L is five or less, staging offers little in performance advantage. See Fig. 17-1.

CHAPTER 18

Refueling
Space Vehicles

A ROCKET CAN accelerate to higher and higher speed as long as it has propellants to burn. Unfortunately, the high thrust requirements of space boosters exhaust the propellant supplies in only a few minutes. If some method could be found to refuel space vehicles in flight, attainable final speed would depend only on the number of times the propellant tanks were refilled. Many methods of refueling space vehicles have been suggested and many will no doubt be tried out in practice in the coming years. A few of the more interesting methods will be discussed in this chapter.

Most of the more important refueling techniques could be grouped under the headings suborbital, orbital, in transit, libration point, lunar orbital and lunar. Various possibilities exist within each of these categories.

Suborbital refueling might be accomplished at speeds between about 18,000 and 24,000 feet per second with Dyna Soar-type lifting vehicles. Ranges varying from 5000 to 25,000 miles and times of flight from one-half to one and one-half hours would allow sufficient time for refueling operations if problems of simultaneous launch and rendezvous can be solved.

Another type of suborbital refueling could be carried out with the aid of air-breathing engines. For example, a rocket engine might be used to boost a lifting vehicle to perhaps 5000 feet per second. At this speed a fixed-geometry ramjet would take over for a cruise period during which propellant tanks would be refilled. Then the rocket engine would be used once more to accelerate the vehicle to orbit. In this way, a single-stage vehicle could fly into orbit using current chemical propulsion techniques! *

A space vehicle might be refueled in near-earth orbit from a tanker vehicle or at an orbiting space station. Very accurate guidance is needed for either method, but the guidance equipment already designed for the ICBM's should be sufficiently accurate for this purpose. The Gemini, two-man space vehicles are planned to be used for testing these rendezvous techniques.

Orbital rendezvous of manned vehicles should be very much easier than with unmanned payloads and will probably prove to be not as difficult as most people have supposed. The booster guidance system should be able to direct the orbiting space ships to within a mile or two of each other, after which the pilot or pilots will gradually maneuver the ships together in much the same manner as ocean ships or manned aircraft are steered into close proximity or contact. Actually, the space rendezvous should be easier since there is no turbulence of air or water to produce erratic motions of the vehicles. Although laymen may be disturbed by the thought of a rendezvous at such high speeds, a moment's thought should convince them that it is only the relative speed between the vehicles which is important. The fact that we are all moving with the earth around the sun at 18 miles per second is of no consequence in performing a rendezvous on the dance floor!

Even some scientists and engineers have been disturbed by the fact that a vehicle trying to overtake another vehicle in orbit would find that an increase in speed would cause him to rise into a higher orbit because of the increased centrifugal force. This would be a

* This technique was suggested by C. Lindley of the Marquardt Corporation in a conversation with one of the authors.

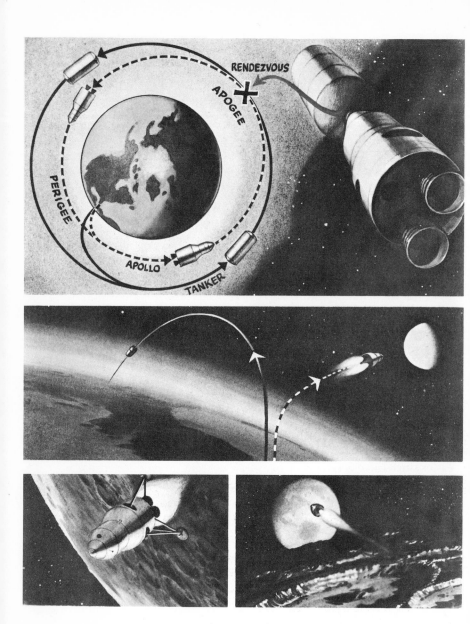

Fig. 18-1   Earth orbit rendezvous. An Apollo vehicle is shown being refueled by a tanker, then leaving earth orbit for the moon, landing on the moon and returning from the moon.

problem and a learning process would be required, but it would actually not be very different from aerodynamic flight. Here the aerodynamic lift of a vehicle increases with speed and a pilot attempting to overtake another aircraft would rise to higher altitude if he did not decrease his angle of attack at the same time that he increased his speed.

Many varieties of orbital refueling have been suggested, including refueling with air scooped up by special collector vehicles and refueling with propellants carried from the moon or the asteroids (less energy required than for hauling from earth). Any such method, if successful, could completely change the economics of space transportation.

Note that a one-stage, advanced nuclear vehicle capable of carrying one-third of its gross weight into orbit as payload (assume propellant fraction of 0.5 and $I_{sp} = 2300$ stapps) could be refueled by one other similar vehicle and then could proceed to carry the same payload to the surface of the moon and back to the earth. It might also be noted that if a similar propulsion system could be used in a vehicle with a propellant fraction of 0.85 instead of 0.5, then the entire trip could be made without refueling!

Just as with staging, the additional complexity of refueling operations is only worth the price when the mission velocity requirements are very high compared to the vehicle propulsion capabilities. When specific impulse and propellant fraction are sufficiently high compared to the mission velocity that gross weight-to-payload ratios can be kept down to five or less, staging or refueling is probably not worth the trouble.

There could be some advantages in refueling on the way to the moon rather than in orbit close to the earth. There are also some obvious disadvantages. If the mission vehicle and one or more tanker vehicles are fired from the earth at escape velocity, rendezvous and refueling operations could be conducted while on the way to the moon.

Proponents of this method argue that total time in space would be reduced since the additional time for orbital rendezvous would not be required, guidance problems would be simpler since two or three days could be spent on the maneuver and rendezvous propulsion requirements would be reduced for the same reason.

An obvious disadvantage is that the minimum size of the booster must be larger to boost the payload to escape velocity rather than to orbit. Also, the vehicles must be launched simultaneously from separate launch facilities rather than in sequence from the same pad. An even more serious disadvantage is that of recall time or abort safety.

If something goes wrong during orbital refueling and a decision is made to abort the mission, the astronaut can be brought down within an hour or two. The point of no return is not crossed until after the refueling has taken place and the vehicle is on its way to the moon (with everything it needs for the return trip).

The latter objection on abort safety also applies to the methods of refueling at the libration point, lunar orbit or on the lunar surface. However, the libration point method does not require simultaneous launch.

In using this method a space vehicle would proceed to the null gravity point and wait there for the other vehicles involved in the operation. It is inferior to the orbital rendezvous in terms of abort safety but superior to lunar rendezvous in this respect since very little fuel would be required to initiate the fall back to the earth. One important disadvantage of this method would be that it would be restricted to minimum energy transits. At least high-speed trips would be more expensive in fuel if it were necessary to decelerate with retro thrust at the libration point.

Rendezvous in lunar orbit also provides some advantages. One use of this technique would be that of leaving propellant tanks or complete propulsion units in orbit before making the descent to the lunar surface. These units would then be picked up again on the way out to be used for the return trip. In this way we would save the energy required to carry this mass down to the surface of the moon and back up again to orbit. Thus its total velocity change need only be 6000 feet per second instead of 16,000 feet per second. The difference in energy per pound involved is a factor of seven!

Assume that a two-stage vehicle is designed to land on the moon and then take off again after being carried to escape velocity by a large booster. The two-stage vehicle has a gross weight of 180,000 pounds and each stage has a payload ratio of three. Thus the return payload is 180,000 divided by nine or 20,000 pounds. A velocity change of 8000 feet per second is assumed for each stage with an exhaust velocity of 10,000 feet per second and a propellant fraction of 0.85.

Now suppose that the velocity change required for each stage were only 5000 feet per second instead of 8000. Then the payload ratio per stage would be only two instead of three, and the return payload would be one-fourth of the total rather than one-ninth. However, we are ignoring the propellants needed to go into lunar orbit and out again.

It would be necessary to have a vehicle weighing 80,000 pounds in lunar orbit in order to carry 20,000 pounds down to the surface and back again to orbit. It would require 12,000 pounds to accelerate the payload out of orbit and back to earth. Thus it would be necessary to place a total of 92,000 pounds in orbit of which 12,000 pounds would be left behind for the final acceleration back to earth. The total mass required at escape velocity would then be approximately 150,000 pounds as compared to 180,000 pounds by the direct method. Since the mass of the booster at earth launch may be some 80 times the escape mass, this difference of 30,000 pounds could mean a difference of 2.5 million pounds in booster mass. This might mean a difference of two F–1 engines in the first stage cluster.*

Rendezvous on the surface of the moon rather than in space has some advantages and also some obvious disadvantages. Perhaps the greatest advantage of the lunar rendezvous is that a payload once safely landed would stay at its landing point. Its future position would not be a function of time and thus no time requirements

---

* At the time of this writing, the lunar orbit rendezvous method, called LOR, has been selected for the Apollo program. By cutting the crew from three men down to two and using this method, it is believed that a single Saturn C–5 will be sufficient for the moon trip rather than the two formerly planned for EOR (Earth Orbit Rendezvous).

would be placed on the launch of subsequent payloads. The condition and position of each unmanned payload could be checked by telemetry after it had been landed on the moon. Only after sufficient propellants and supplies had been landed within a reasonably small target area would the manned vehicle be sent. It would then be necessary for the men to gather and assemble the necessary materials for their return trip. This could be done solely by manpower far more easily on the moon, because of its low gravity, than could be done on the earth.

Of course, there are a number of uncertainties about the lunar environment which make this method appear unattractive at this time. The most important of these is perhaps the general question of individual protection when outside the space ship or base living quarters. Will it be safe to move around on the moon in any sort of space suit? If so, how massive and cumbersome must it be? If the lunar explorers must move around on the surface only inside some tank-like vehicle, then the difficulty of assembling a return vehicle from widely scattered components would be greatly increased. It is uncertainty of this type which has made the early moon-trip planners shy away from this method. Of course, there is the obvious disadvantage that the maximum size of a landing unit must be only about one-tenth the mass of payload which can be boosted to orbit. Thus, larger manned vehicles could always be used for orbital assembly and refueling than for lunar rendezvous.

Of all the methods that have been suggested, that of refueling in close earth orbit may prove to be the best for a wide range of deep space operations. Since it can be accomplished with smaller boosters than the other space rendezvous techniques, it will probably be tried first and successfully accomplished first. Titan II, Atlas Centaur, Saturn C–1 and Vostok all have sufficient payload capability for this mission. It may be that even before these words are in print Russia will have already accomplished the first manned orbital rendezvous maneuvers and be in the process of assembling a vehicle for manned lunar flight! *

* Vostok III and IV came within three miles of each other in August, 1962, after the above had been written.

CHAPTER 19

Present and Future
Space Boosters

THE KEY TO space travel is the booster vehicle. Although the booster alone would be useless without the payload or space capsule and an adequate guidance system, it has been the difficult and costly problem of developing the primary booster hardware itself, engines, tanks, controls, etc., which has delayed the coming of the space age.

Now we know that the age of manned space travel is here and that great achievements lie just ahead. What can we expect in the future development of large space boosters? Today we have Atlas, Titan, Saturn C–1 and Vostok. What will we have tomorrow?

First, suppose we consider the probable increase in take-off mass and thrust for Russian and U.S. space boosters.

EXPECTED GROWTH IN VEHICLE MASS

Figure 19-1 shows the past growth in rocket vehicle mass and the expected increase in the future. The ordinate of the graph (logarithmic scale) shows vehicle mass in pounds. The abscissa gives time in years. After an initial period of learning from the German V–2, both Russian and U.S. progress appears to follow a normal logarithmic growth pattern and thus can be represented by straight lines on semilog paper. On standard grid paper these lines would

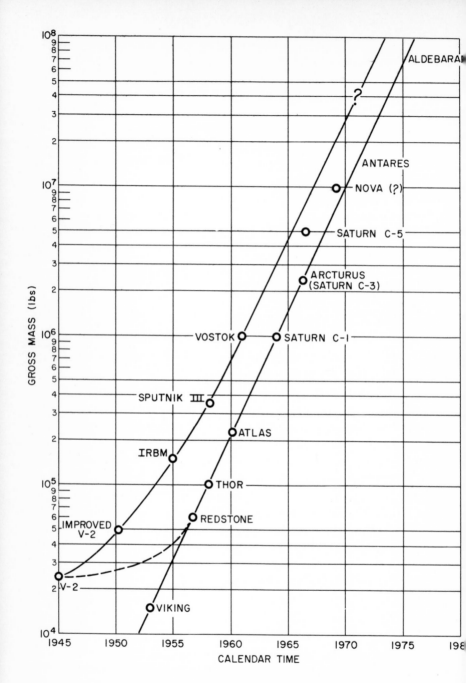

Fig. 19-1   Increase in mass of U.S. and Russian rockets.

curve rapidly upward in the manner familiar to those who have studied population growth.

The Russian curve advances from their early redesign of the captured V–2, through the Sputnik booster to the Vostok booster, and on up to the expected large space boosters of the future. The Sputnik booster probably had about 500,000 pounds take-off thrust and a gross mass of about 350,000 pounds. At this mass, its payload ratio for Sputnik III was approximately 115.

The Vostok booster and the Venus probe booster are probably very similar in size to Saturn C–1 with a thrust of 1.32 million pounds and a mass of one million pounds. Its payload ratio for the Venus probe orbital payload of 14,000 pounds would have been close to 70.

The thrust of the Vostok booster has been estimated by some U.S. experts to be 800,000 pounds. This figure has been so widely quoted that it has come to be accepted as a fact, although no Russian statement has ever been made to support this figure. On the contrary, official Russian statements support a higher total first-stage thrust.

The official Russian description of the Vostok booster strongly implied that the first stage had six engines. It has been generally assumed for many years that their basic engine had an original design thrust of 100 metric tons or 220,000 pounds. Six of these engines would produce a total thrust of 1.32 million pounds.

The official Russian statement also noted a take-off horsepower of 20,000,000. This is equivalent to 11×10^9 foot-pounds per second. If the Vostok propellant is assumed to be lox and kerosene (as has been officially stated by Russia) with a take-off specific impulse of 250 stapps and an exhaust velocity of 8000 feet per second, total thrust can be found from power divided by exhaust velocity to be 1.37 million pounds.

It should be noted that a take-off thrust of 800,000 pounds and a gross mass of about 500,000 pounds, which are the values commonly assumed for the Vostok launcher, indicate a *more efficient* vehicle than any 1961 model U.S. rocket. Ever since the first Sputnik it has been generally agreed in the western world that the

Russian rockets were *less efficient* than the U.S. models in terms of payload ratio.

Professor Oberth was quoted as stating that the Russians built alarm clocks while we built ladies' wrist watches. It has been assumed that they achieved higher reliability by building larger and heavier vehicles, with some loss in performance as compared to our own designs.

However, a gross mass of 500,000 pounds used to boost 14,000 pounds into orbit would mean a payload ratio of 36, which is just about twice as good as we had managed by the same period (Midas II launched in 1960 had a payload mass of 3500 pounds and a gross mass of 240,000 pounds). Saturn C–1 is expected to have a payload ratio of approximately 50. Titan II may go down to about 40. The original design of Saturn C–2 had a payload ratio of 25, but this was achieved by the use of hydrogen-oxygen upper stages, something not generally credited to the Russians for 1961-operation vehicles.

A fairly obvious and logical design approach which Russia might have used for Vostok would be a combination of three ICBM vehicles into a laterally staged vehicle.

Suppose that the first stage of their ICBM vehicle used two R–14 engines with a thrust of 220,000 pounds each. Suppose also that their ICBM was similar to our Titan except for this somewhat higher thrust—a total of 440,000 pounds compared to 300,000. Now three of the ICBM first stages could be clustered to form a laterally staged booster with six engines and three pairs of propellant tanks.

Using the cross-pumping method, all three engines would be supplied from the outer tanks until these were empty, then the outer two units would drop off. The central vehicle would then continue as the second stage. With only these two stages it would seem feasible to carry the 10,000 pound Vostok capsule into orbit. The 14,000-pound payload used in connection with the Venus probe could have been boosted by the Vostok launcher plus a third stage.

The Russian rocket growth curve has led the U.S. curve by two to three years since the late 1940's. It will probably continue to do so unless our space program is greatly accelerated. At the time of writing it appears probable that Saturn C–5 may be accelerated sufficiently to close the gap by about 1967.

The U.S. program, starting with Viking and Redstone, has grown through the Atlas and Titan vehicles to the present experimental Saturn C–1. This vehicle at one million pounds gross weight and 1.5 million pounds thrust is to have a capability for lifting 20,000 pounds to orbit.

The Arcturus, indicated in Fig. 19-1, and pictured on Fig. 19-2, is a conceptual vehicle weighing approximately 2.5 million pounds with a thrust of 3.0 million pounds from two F–1 engines. It would have a capability for lifting approximately 100,000 pounds to orbit.

Fig. 19-2 Arcturus. A conceptual vehicle similar to the Saturn C-3 based on clustered Titan tanks and two F-1 booster engines.

Illus.: Martin Company

Recently, a vehicle similar to Arcturus was being considered by NASA for the Apollo circumlunar mission. This was the Saturn C–3.

The NOVA design was still not frozen at the time of writing, but would presumably use eight to ten F–1 engines in its first stage with possibly a Saturn C–3 booster for its second stage. The second stage of the C–3 and the third stage of NOVA would be powered by a cluster of J–2, liquid-hydrogen, liquid-oxygen engines. Each of these engines will have a thrust of 200,000 pounds. A cluster of four may be used.

Beyond NOVA, two advanced conceptual vehicles, the Antares and the Aldebaran, have been indicated on the graph. Antares is powered by air-breathing engines in its first flight phase, and a Rover or Nerva nuclear engine in its second propulsion phase.

The Queen Mary-sized Aldebaran is powered by an advanced nuclear propulsion system.

The growth in vehicle mass indicated here may take place, first of all, to provide practical-sized space payloads. The second reason for growth is to improve the payload fraction and the vehicle efficiency. Still a third reason for size increase is to reduce costs. While payload mass increases even faster than gross mass as the vehicle is enlarged, the over-all cost per pound of the vehicle decreases. Thus the vehicle cost per pound of payload is reduced drastically.

ANTICIPATED INCREASE IN SPECIFIC IMPULSE

Another basic trend that will have profound effects on vehicle performance and payload transportation costs is the increase in specific impulse and exhaust velocity. As indicated in Fig. 19-3, expected improvements in this basic space booster capability will have dramatic effects on the vehicle payload ratio.

At an exhaust velocity of 10,000 feet per second (current capability) it is just possible to achieve lunar landing although payload ratios are poor. With a four-stage vehicle, $G/L = 410$, and for three stages, 680.

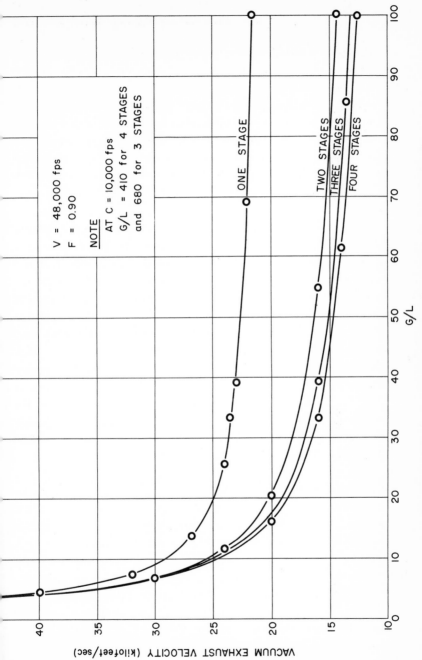

Fig. 19-3 Effects of exhaust velocity on payload for soft lunar landing.

However, if exhaust velocity for all stages was raised to 13,000 feet per second (hydrogen-oxygen), the payload ratio for a four-stage vehicle would drop to 87 and with maximum capability for chemical propellants ($\sim$15,000 feet per second) to perhaps 50.

Thus we might expect engineering improvements of chemical rockets to eventually provide us with lunar landing performance approximating our present close-orbit capabilities, even without the introduction of new types of propulsion.

Introduction of Rover-type nuclear systems would bring the payload ratio down to 20 for two-stage systems even for very conservative exhaust velocities (20,000 feet per second). More probable early capability of 25,000 feet per second will drop G/L to ten, and reasonably advanced Rover performance of 35,000 feet per second drops the ratio to five for two-stage vehicles and six for one-stage. Note that at this propulsion performance level there is no discernible difference (Fig. 19-3) between the capability of two- and four-stage vehicles and only a 20% difference for one-stage.

It is entirely possible that solid nuclear reactors will eventually develop exhaust velocities of 45,000 feet per second and payload ratios for earth-moon flight will drop to less than four. At this point there will no longer be any discernible advantage in using more than one stage. Advanced nuclear propulsion systems, such as the fusion reactor, the gaseous core reactor or the bomb propulsion system, theoretically would have exhaust velocities of 30,-000 to 60,000 feet per second and payload ratios would drop as low as two.

Now how quickly can we expect these advances to take place? Figure 19-4 indicates that the 1960 capability for exhaust velocities of 10,000 feet per second will have increased to about 13,000 feet per second by 1966 through change to hydrogen and oxygen. By 1972 air-breathing engines and nuclear upper stages will increase the average exhaust velocity to perhaps 20,000 feet per second (conservatively), and by 1976 systems should be in operation with exhaust velocities exceeding 30,000 feet per second.

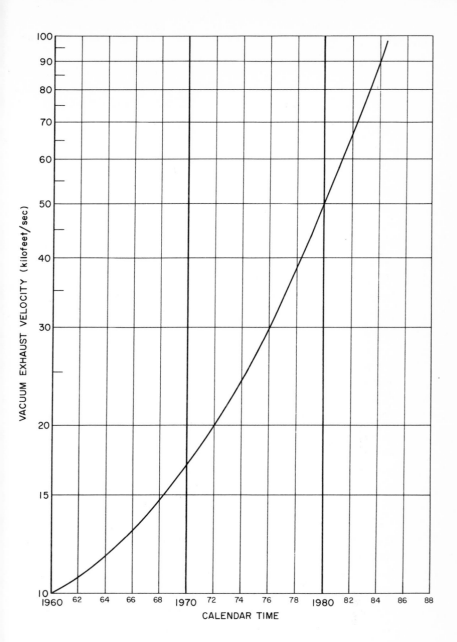

Fig. 19-4 Anticipated increase in propulsion performance.

Note that this curve, which is concave upward on semilog paper, indicates that propulsion performance is improving more rapidly than pure logarithmic growth.

TRENDS IN PAYLOAD CAPABILITIES

In Fig. 19-5 the Russian orbital payload growth curve is compared with the original NASA schedule before the mid-1961 acceleration. Obviously there would have been little chance of overtaking the Russian lead with the old schedule. Although attitudes at the time of writing were more encouraging, the new schedule was not yet crystallized to the point where it could be compared with the Russian curve.

Note that these two growth curves were originally compared in June 1960, long before the launching of Sputnik 7. This payload of 14,000 pounds exactly confirmed the extrapolation of the straight line through Sputniks III and IV.

Of course, we do not know what the Russians will do in space in the future, but the extrapolation of their payload capability as given on Fig. 19-5 is consistent with their statements regarding manned flights to the moon. Yuri Gagarin stated in the summer of 1961 that it might take *as much as* five years for them to get to the moon. Russian scientists were quoted as saying that they would land on the moon in 1964.

As payloads carried to orbit increase, earth-moon payloads will also increase. Figure 19-5 shows the rapid improvement which can be expected to occur in this capability.

Figure 19-6, which was prepared in the summer of 1960, indicates an increase from about 200 pounds in 1961 (Ranger) to 700 pounds in 1963 (Surveyor) to about 2000 pounds in 1965. Actually, the upper limit of the band indicated was already beginning to look conservative by the time of writing in 1961. Saturn C–5 might have the capability to carry 20,000 pounds to the moon in 1966, rather than 1967–1970 as indicated. Nova may be ready to carry more than 50,000 pounds to the moon before 1970.*

---

* While the long-range predictions may turn out to be conservative, it is now clear that the short-range estimates were optimistic. This is a common occurrence with advanced plans of this type.

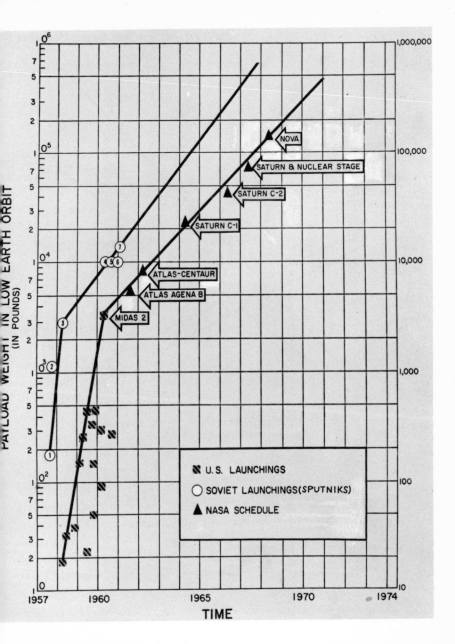

Fig. 19-5 Comparison of trends in U.S. and Russian space payload capabilities.

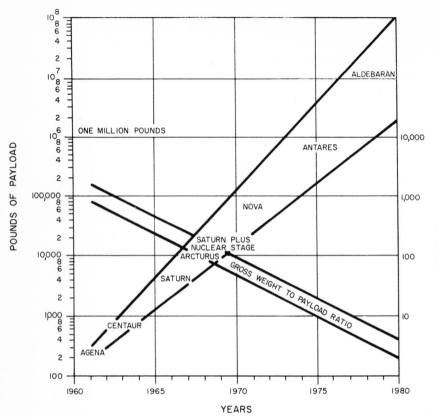

Fig. 19-6

What happens beyond Nova is still a matter for speculation but some possibilities will be discussed in the next section.

ECONOMICAL SPACE VEHICLES

An obvious possibility for the next step beyond Nova is a giant liquid chemical booster on the order of 100 million pounds gross weight. A five-stage vehicle of this size, using liquid hydrogen and oxygen in all stages, might be able to carry as much as one million pounds to the moon. Such a vehicle could be built by 1970 and, perhaps, will be. What would it cost to carry payloads to the moon with such a vehicle?

First, suppose that propellant costs run about five cents per pound. (At three cents per pound for oxygen and 23 cents for hydrogen and a mixture ratio of nine to one.) Then 90 million pounds of propellants would cost approximately five million dollars and the propellant cost per pound of payload would be $5.00.

If there are approximately ten million pounds of structure in the vehicle, we might estimate a structure cost of 100 million dollars or $100.00 per pound of payload. Then the direct operating costs would total $105.00 per pound of payload if no vehicle recovery is assumed.

Suppose however, that all vehicle stages are recovered and re-used 100 times. Then the structure cost is only $1.00 per pound of payload and the total cost is $6.00 per payload pound.

Indirect operating costs for airline flights to Australia were about $3.00 per pound of payload in 1960 for flights taking a total time of two days. Assuming $4.00 for moon flights (there should be no major differences in indirect costs) would result in $10.00 per pound of payload.

Other contenders for the role of the economical space ship are the nuclear space ship Rita, proposed by Douglas, the chemical space plane under study by the USAF, Orion, CONEX and many others. The Antares conceptual vehicle is a nuclear space plane proposed by one of the authors in 1959 as a high-performance vehicle of the 1970–1975 period (see Fig. 19-7).

The Antares was considered to have a gross mass between ten and 20 million pounds. Since it would land and take off horizontally and was a winged aerodynamic vehicle, its propellant fraction was assumed to be only 0.75 as compared to 0.90 or higher for a rocket. The average specific impulse was estimated to be 1000 stapps and the gross weight-to-payload ratio for orbital flight was calculated as four. This calculation assumed a boost to 2000 feet per second by a carrier vehicle on an inclined track. At 2000 feet per second, ramjet engines would be started and would accelerate

Fig. 19-7 A single stage "aerospace" plane combining a cluster of ramjet engines and a single nuclear engine.

Illus.: Martin Company

the vehicle to 8000 to 10,000 feet per second after which the nuclear engine would propel the space plane into orbit.

From orbit to the moon a vehicle like Antares could carry payloads equal to more than 40% of its gross mass. This could be an Antares refueled in orbit or a special ferry vehicle designed for operation from orbit to the moon. In the latter case payload could be an even larger percentage of the gross mass—perhaps as much as 50% ($G/L = 2$). Thus the over-all payload ratio for the earth-moon trip would be eight or ten as compared to 100 for the all-chemical rocket.

For a ten-million-pound Antares (two stages) better than one million pounds of payload could be carried to the moon. Of the nine million pounds of vehicle and propellant, 6.75 million would be liquid hydrogen. At 23 cents per pound, the total propellant cost would be $1,550,000.00 or $1.55 per pound of payload.

If Antares were designed for 100 flights (compared to 10,000 for commercial airliners), the vehicle could cost one billion dollars and still have only $1.00 per payload pound of vehicle depreciation cost. With about $1.50 for propellants and $4.00 for indirect costs, the total cost per pound would be $6.50.

The Aldebaran, proposed by one of the authors in 1959, is a 100-million-pound space plane designed for horizontal take-off and landing from the ocean. Its propulsion was considered to be an advanced nuclear system such as the gaseous core reactor, a fusion reactor, Orion or CONEX. Its specific impulse was estimated at 1500 to 3000 stapps and its propellant fraction at 0.5 to 0.7. At 1500 stapps and 0.5 propellant fraction, Aldebaran would be competitive with Antares. At 3000 stapps and 0.7, its payload fraction for orbital flights would be about 1.6 and for moon flights about five. Total costs per pound of payload would be equal to or less than the costs for Antares (see Fig. 19-8).

Although costs of $10.00 or less per pound delivered to the moon may seem fantastically low to many people who are aware of current, high, space payload costs, it is none the less reasonable to expect such cost reductions in the next 20 years. With cost of perhaps $5000.00 per pound expected for 1965, it appears probable that a drop of an order of magnitude will occur every five

Fig. 19-8 Aldebaran. A conceptual 50,000-ton space ship employing advanced nuclear propulsion.

Illus.: Martin Company

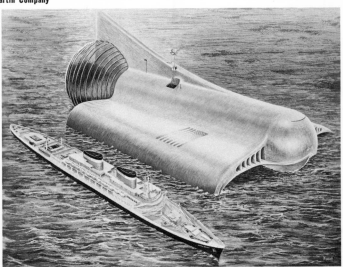

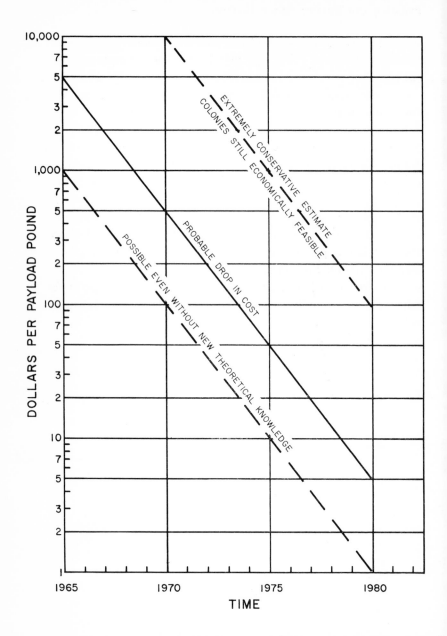

Fig. 19-9 Earth-Moon transportation costs.

years. At this rate moon travel will cost only $50.00 per pound in 1975 and $5.00 in 1980 (see Fig. 19-9). Some people estimate a slightly less precipitous drop with an order of magnitude change every seven years. This would mean $50.00 per pound in 1979 and $5.00 in 1986.

Dr. Wernher von Braun stated in testimony to Congress that costs should be about $3000.00 per pound in 1967 and $100.00 to $200.00 in 1975. This is a factor of 15 to 30 drop in eight years. At that rate, by 1983 the cost would be down to $5.00 to $15.00 per pound. Whichever of these estimates is taken, it should be clear that interplanetary travel in the latter part of this century will be no more costly than the intercontinental air travel of the 1960's. This should not be surprising since the energy requirements for round trips to the moon (approximately 53,000 feet per second) are not significantly greater than for round trips to the other side of the earth (approximately 50,000 feet per second for two-way ballistic flight).

CHAPTER **20**

Life in Space

IN THE SEARCH for life in space it is first necessary to define what we mean by life and set down the criteria for this type of life. To find life as we know it, we must look for a form recognizable to us. This, in turn, means that essentially we are looking for something like ourselves or creatures comparable to those familiar to us. The keystone of this earth life is the carbon atom. Chemists tell us that carbon is tetravalent—meaning it can combine quite readily with four other atoms. It is this curious combining property that gives rise to the long chains of molecular compounds which make up life. But again this is a life with which we are familiar.

It is possible to postulate a hypothetical type of life built on the silicon atom or some other multivalent atom, as some have suggested, but the form based on the silicon atom may be such that we may never recognize it. Although we cannot say it cannot exist, until such time as we have come into contact with it so that a decision must be made we can by-pass this problem.

Thus, in this search for extra-terrestrial life, we begin by postulating a life similar to our own. For this type of earth-life we can set down certain criteria which must be fulfilled.

252

CONDITIONS FOR A TERRESTRIAL LIFE

In the universe we find a tremendous range of temperatures from perhaps billions of degress in the centers of some stars to a few degrees above the absolute zero for interstellar space. In this enormous gamut of temperatures there is a narrow, thin range which can support life like ours. This range runs from about 100 degrees below to about 200 degrees above zero. There is an even narrower belt in which this life could have begun, certainly not more than half the range given above.

In the body are found large complex protein molecules called *enzymes*. These permit body reactions to take place at an optimum rate at a lower temperature. If we raise the temperature, the reaction rates increase. However, enzymes are unstable and go to irreversible destruction when subjected to excessive heat. Thus, if temperatures go high enough, life cannot begin nor be sustained.

Run the temperature down too low and the water in the cells will crystallize and the cells will die. Run the temperature up too high and the water in the cells will evaporate and again the cells will die. Thus moderate temperatures are a necessity for the beginning and the continuance of life.

Water, the universal solvent, is essential for earth-life. Wherever we expect to find life, we must find copious quantities of water. The human body is about 70% water by weight. The unusually-high specific heat of water permits the body to maintain a nearly constant temperature. The high latent heat of water makes it an ideal regulating mechanism for stability in body temperatures.

The third criterion usually accepted for life is the presence of an atmosphere including oxygen. This vital gas is necessary for the oxidation of food to provide energy for the body. Through the medium of the blood stream it also functions to rid the body of metabolic wastes.

So critical are these demands that many scientists believe that all of them must be met. The lack of a single condition may preclude the possibility of life's beginning or existing on a planet.

Having established the criteria for life, let us explore the solar system to see whether we can find any place other than the earth where life can exist.

Dr. Hubertus Strughold has given the name of *ecosphere* to the life-supporting zone in a planetary system. He defines this zone as the one in which we should find gaseous oxygen and water as a liquid.

LIFE IN THE SOLAR SYSTEM

If we examine the extent of this ecosphere in the solar system, we find that only three planets fulfill the necessary conditions. Venus is on the inner boundary. Mars represents the outer boundary and, of course, between lies the earth. Mercury, the planet closest to the sun, cannot support life, according to Strughold's theory, for this planet is only 3100 miles in diameter and of such small mass that the velocity of escape from the planet is so low that any atmosphere which it may have had in the past has long since been dissipated into interplanetary space. Beyond Mars we find the major planets of which the closest is Jupiter. This object is about five times as far from the sun as is the earth; thus it receives much less radiation than the earth. At the top of the cloud belts on Jupiter the temperature has gone down to −200° F. Even with a solid surface at this temperature life could not begin or exist. However, as noted in chapter 6, Jupiter may have a warm or hot surface covered by clouds of ammonia and methane. Some astronomers believe these conditions could be conducive to the evolution of a form of life. All the planets beyond Jupiter, except Pluto, may be viewed in the same light.

On November 30, 1959 an astronomical event of marked significance took place. A high-flying balloon took spectrograms of Venus which disclosed the presence of water vapor in the planetary atmosphere. This means that both carbon dioxide and water vapor are present on Venus. The significance of this finding is that with carbon dioxide, water and radiation it may be possible to synthesize the amino acids which may be considered the building blocks of the protein molecule. In the long ago—some four to five billion years ago—these elements, in addition to ammonia and methane, were present on the earth. Within a period of about two billion years, the early amino acids developed into the first single-celled creature on earth. The carbon remains of these creatures are found buried in rocks some 2.5 billion years old.

Thus it would appear that if temperatures are of the proper order, life could have begun on Venus. In the past, from purely theoretical considerations, astronomers have accepted the surface temperature of Venus as being on the order of 150 to 200 degrees Fahrenheit.

However, as we have discovered on page 74, the close passage of the Mariner 2 probe has yielded a surface temperature of about 800°F. This temperature indicates the complete lack of liquid water on the surface of the planet. The absence of water combined with an 800°F temperature would preclude the formation of any type of life which we could assume would be like ours. It is highly improbable that any life exists on Venus.

Beyond the earth we find Mars. Of about one-half the diameter of the earth and of much lower mass, Mars has a surface gravity too small to maintain an atmosphere of a density comparable to that of the earth. Astronomers are generally agreed that the atmospheric pressure on the Martian surface is about ten per cent of what it is on the earth's surface. This low pressure could not permit the formation or continuance of a life like ours. What atmosphere is present is most probably composed of nitrogen with some argon as a contaminant.

Until recently, the only compound found spectroscopically on Mars was carbon dioxide. The polar caps are quite definitely water in the form of hoarfrost, as determined by Dr. Gerard P. Kuiper from infrared spectrograms taken in 1948. This hoarfrost sublimes into the atmosphere when the polar caps disappear. The total amount of water in the atmosphere, according to Dr. Gerard de Vaucouleurs, is about 1/250th of an inch at surface conditions.

Oxygen can be inferred as being present in the Martian atmosphere from the presence of vegetation. If present, it is there in such insignificant amount as to defy detection.

In addition to the low atmospheric pressure, we find rather severe temperatures on the surface. On the equator—where the temperature is highest shortly after noon—the temperatures go as high as 85 degrees Fahrenheit, whereas at night, at the same place, the temperature falls to about 100 degrees below zero. These are severe temperature ranges, but they are no more severe than those found at the South Pole. Thus, although life may not have evolved there, certainly it could persist if humans visit the planet.

There is considerable evidence that a vegetable life is present on Mars. There is no evidence that animal life has evolved there; in fact, all evidence indicates that animal life could not have developed to a high order on this planet.[*] If there is animal life there, we can be assured that it did not evolve along the same pattern as on the earth. It would have had to adapt to the peculiar conditions of Mars.

So in our solar system we find positive evidence of animal life only on the earth. We have found evidence of a form of vegetable life on Mars with a small possibility of a low form of animal life also existing there. Venus, as has been indicated, has a small probability of life—certainly not like ours.

LIFE BEYOND THE SOLAR SYSTEM

What about life beyond the solar system? Until quite recently, it was possible to draw some statistical pictures of what might be found in space, but the baseline on which astronomers extrapolated was so short that the conclusions left a great deal to be desired. Some significant work on this problem has been done by Dr. Su-Shu Huang.

---

[*] To close the ecological cycle, Dr. Levitt has postulated a form of animal life for Mars. A full description may be found in I. M. Levitt, *A Space Traveler's Guide to Mars* (New York: Holt, Rinehart, and Winston), 1956.

When we go outside the solar system, direct evidence is lacking concerning the possibility of life, and except for some exotic proposals to launch a Celestial Noah's Ark at some date far in the future, this may never be definitive. However, there are certain criteria which can be laid down as to the adaptability of an area in the sky suitable for life.

Dr. Huang echoes the thoughts of biologists that the evolution of something as complex as a human being takes a long period of time—on the order of several billion years. If we accept this assumption, and all our knowledge points to this as a valid assumption, it means that only those stars whose lifetimes are on the order of five to ten billion years can furnish the steady flow of energy for the period of time necessary for life to evolve.

Once this assumption has been made, we can eliminate those stars which are exceedingly bright or exceedingly faint. The bright stars give off energy at such a prodigious rate that they cannot last for more than a few hundred thousand years to hundreds of millions of years. By the same token, the faint stars can certainly live long enough—their lifetimes are on the order of hundreds of billions of years—but the habitable zones around the stars, the ecospheres, shrink so that the chances of finding planets in these zones are vanishingly small.

Thus we are limited to certain stars on the main sequence which are not too bright and not too faint. These stars range from an F 5 star through the G class and down to a K 5 star. This is the realm in which we must look for stars which can support life.

Dr. Otto Struve has pointed out that the rapid axial rotation of the main sequence stars stops rather abruptly at spectral-type F 5. If one were to ask what has happened to the angular momentum of these stars, a reasonable answer might be that the angular momentum has, in some mysterious fashion, been transferred to the planets that have evolved around these stars.

In the case of our sun, we find it possesses 99.8% of the mass of the system but only two per cent of the angular momentum. Most of this angular momentum resides in the distant, fast-spinning major planets. It may well be that this criterion reduces the possible number of stars that can harbor life.

There is still another factor which reduces the possible number of planetary systems in space—the number of double stars. More and more astronomers are becoming convinced that at least half the stars in the sky are double stars. At this time there is no way of differentiating between double stars and stars with planetary systems, but it must be noted that a stable planetary orbit around a double star system suitable for the evolution of life is highly unlikely. Thus we can eliminate these.

Even with the elimination of these stellar groups, there are still many places where life can develop.

CONDITIONS ON THE NEAREST STARS

In order to find out whether these stars which fit the criteria above do harbor life or at least are suitable for life, we can investigate those about which we know most—the nearest stars.

At the Sproul Observatory of Swarthmore College, astronomers have closely investigated all stars within 16 light-years of the earth. In this volume of space they find some 55 stars.

When we explore this region of space it becomes instantly apparent that the majority of stars close to the sun are faint. In fact, only three stars, Sirius, Procyon and Altair, are brighter than the sun. These stars are also bigger than the sun. By actual measurement we find Sirius 23 times as bright as the sun, whereas Altair is eight and Procyon six times brighter than our sun. If we look for faint stars, we find one only 1/50,000th as bright as the sun.

Of the total of 55 stars, 51 are fainter than the sun. Only eight of the stars can be seen without telescopic aid. In addition to the stars already mentioned, only Alpha Centauri, the nearest star in the sky, is well-known. The other four are obscure faint stars named *tau Ceti, epsilon Eridani, omicron-two Eridani* and, finally, *epsilon Indi.*

It is significant that the majority of the stars close to the sun are faint. It the past, we thought that the bright stars were the nearer

stars. On the average this may be true, but certainly in the vicinity
of the sun this is not true.

Most of the stars in the vicinity of the sun are less than one-
hundredth as bright as our sun. Not only are the stars fainter, but
they are also cooler, that is, redder. Only three stars of the 50
are hotter than the sun. Three stars are just as hot as the sun,
whereas all the others are cooler. In addition to these 50 normal
stars, there are also five white dwarfs. These are a curious class of
tiny, massive stars with extraordinarily high densities, some on the
order of a ton per cubic inch.

From the double stars in the vicinity of the sun we can get some
indication of the mass of the stars in terms of the sun's mass.
When these are computed, it is found that the heaviest star is
Sirius, with a mass 2.3 times that of the sun. The other stars have
smaller masses dropping down to about ⅟₂₅th the mass of the sun.

Dr. Peter van de Kamp, Director of the Sproul Observatory,
has prepared an intriguing model to represent the population of
space in the immediate vicinity of the sun. He assumes a sphere
of space 16 light-years in diameter compressed into a ball the size
of the earth. In this earth he would place 55 objects to represent
the nearest stars. In size they would consist of tennis balls, golf
balls, marbles and smaller objects. There would be nine pairs of
balls. These are the double systems in which the two components
would be slightly more than one-half mile apart. There would be
three triple systems with about the same spacing between the
three components. Of the remainder, we believe that 26 are single
balls. However, subsequent observations may disclose the presence
of faint companions or even planetary systems around these single
stars.

The important point is that in a ball the size of the earth we find
only 55 stars or star systems whose greatest size would be that of
a tennis ball. On this scale the earth would be the size of a tiny
grain of sand.

Using Dr. van de Kamp's data, we can explore his findings to
disclose stars with planetary systems possibly suitable for the forma-

tion of life. If we exclude all stars hotter than F 5 and cooler than K 5 and all multiple systems, we find that there remain only four stars. These are *epsilon Eridani, epsilon Indi, tau Ceti* and *Groombridge* 1618.

Unfortunately, *epsilon Indi* is an intrinsically faint star having a luminosity 12% that of the sun. Although this does not rule out the possibility of life, it restricts the ecosphere to such narrow limits that it is doubtful that a planet could be found in this belt. By the same token, *Groombridge* 1618 has a luminosity only three-hundredths that of the sun, and the ecosphere is even smaller. Thus these two stars can be eliminated as places where life can occur.

Only two stars remain—*tau Ceti* and *epsilon Eridani*—as the only stars which could support a planetary system where life might be found. Tau Ceti, a star of spectral class G 4, is 11.8 light-years from the earth; its luminosity is 38% that of the sun. Epsilon Eridani is a K 2 star about 10.8 light-years from the earth. It has a luminosity 34% that of the sun. Thus these two stars with their lower luminosity also have smaller ecospheres but these are not impossibly small. These then, are the only places within a reasonable distance where astronomers can look into the sky for evidence of life in the universe.

STATISTICS AND LIFE

There is a statistical approach to this problem. Recently, one of the authors has been going through the Schlesinger Bright Star Catalogue to tabulate the stars in the different spectral classes. Of the first 5000 stars chosen, it was found that approximately 3000 fell into that class of stars in which life is highly improbable. The other 40% consisted of the stars in spectral class from F 5 to K 5, the range in which life is possible. This range appears to be greater than can be found in the Hertzsprung-Russell diagram, but it must be remembered that we are not working with a true sample of space. In the bright star catalogue we are choosing stars by their apparent brightnesses and not their distance from the earth.

Of these 5000 stars, 1996 have potential for planets supporting life. This percentage is so great that it cannot be the true picture. If you will recall that in the sphere of space centered on the sun and 16 light-years in radius we found only 55 stars. Of these 55 stars, only three were capable of supporting life. When we apply this correction to the 40% from the bright star catalogue, we find that two per cent or 110 of the 5000 stars could have planetary systems in which there is a possibility of life.

It should be stressed that these are preliminary results, and it can be assumed that in a subsequent survey which is planned using stellar distances as the criterion, instead of the apparent brightnesses of the stars, in all probability that two per cent may fall to perhaps one-fourth of one per cent. This one-fourth per cent would then represent the number of stars possibly possessing planetary systems on which life could have started.

In our Milky Way system, there are about 100 billion stars. Using the factor arrived at above, we find that 250 million stars in our galaxy may possess planetary systems. It is estimated that at least a billion galaxies can be reached with our largest telescope. This space is what is called the observable universe. Thus in the observable universe there may be 250 million billion planetary systems. What is the possibility of intelligent life on these planetary systems?

PROJECT OZMA

In 1960 Dr. Philip Morrison and Dr. Giuseppe Cocconi, both of Cornell University, proposed that we try to reach planetary systems around other stars by listening for radio signals from them. They indicated that:

> The presence of interstellar signals is entirely consistent with all we know and . . . if signals are present the means of detecting them is now at hand. Few will deny the profound importance, practical and philosophical, which the detection of interstellar communications would have. We, therefore, feel that a discriminating search for signals deserves considerable effort.

The probability of success is difficult to estimate; but if we never search the chance for success is zero.

It may well be that this letter sparked a search begun in 1961 which, as the Cornell scientists indicated, would probably result in failure. In the spring of that year the 85-foot radio telescope of the National Radio Astronomy Observatory at Green Bank, West Virginia went into operation in the first calculated search for extra-terrestrial life.

This project, called Ozma, was named for the legendary Queen of the land of Oz, a distant land, difficult to reach and populated by strange and exotic beings. The radio telescope was directed to the stars *tau Ceti* and *epsilon Eridani,* which, as has been disclosed, represent two of the most likely stars around which planetary systems with life could exist. The search proved futile; no intelligible signals were received from these stars. Yet this 150-hour search sparked a trend of thought among scientists which indicates that the future may see other searches of this type undertaken.

Essentially, what was done was to monitor the signals coming from the stars to try to find some pattern which would be recognizable to us as something which could not have fortuitously happened. The interpretation of these patterns was the most difficult part of the undertaking. The only criterion Dr. Drake used in this search was to look for something which we, on earth, might transmit if we were signalling some other planet. Just what form would these signals take?

First we must assume that they are intelligent beings on these other planets with a rather high level of intelligence. Once having made this assumption we might look for a series of patterns in the radio signals which might have meaning to us. Astronomers indicate that an intelligent message may consist of a series of prime numbers, such as 1, 2, 3, 5, 7. Another form the message could take would be a series of simple arithmetic sums. Even a series of beeps may provide the means for communicating with distant planets. Thus the language of mathematics might provide the basis of communication. It is conceivable that a regular series of sounds which might consist of beep . . . beep beep . . . beep beep beep . . . beep beep beep beep . . . beep . . . beep beep . . . beep beep beep . . . beep beep beep beep . . . etc. may provide the clue to begin this work.

Even if patterns of signals were received indicating that intelligent beings are indeed present in space, we would not only have the difficult task of interpreting them but what is quite disturbing is that even for the stars indicated above we would have to wait about 20 years for the signals to make a round trip. That is, if Project Ozma had succeeded in its mission it would take 20 years after we built the necessary transmitting station to complete an exchange of signals.

There are other factors which reduce the probabilities of the success of this project. In Project Ozma the astronomers recorded signals from the stars for approximately six hours per day over a period of about a month. If by any chance the signals transmitted by the planets of the distant stars had been off the air for that month, we would not have received them. Also, if the period of transmission was in between the six hour observing periods, we would have missed them. When we begin to analyze the situation, we begin to realize that the odds of ever hearing signals like these are so overpowering that one might wonder why astronomers bother with them. This might well be considered an exercise in futility. However, what is more important is that the techniques that are used today may point the way for more powerful equipment in the future and there may come a time when the odds for receiving and interpreting these cosmic signals will not be so forbidding. As long as astronomers are aware of the problem there is always the possibility of a solution. If there is other life in the universe, scientists on this earth may eventually find some means of communicating with this other life.

CHAPTER 21

Our Future
In Space

As the age of manned space flight begins, astronauts and cosmonauts are sent on longer and longer orbital flights and preparations move forward rapidly for the giant step to the moon.

We know that American circumlunar and lunar landing flights as part of the Apollo program are scheduled for the middle years of this decade. Manned, circumlunar flights by Russian cosmonauts may come even as early as 1963. But what follows the landing of men on the moon? Will we go on to establish permanent bases there which will eventually grow into self-sufficient colonies? Or will we make only a few exploratory trips and then return the moon to the astronomer, the poet and the lover?

Of course no one knows the answers to these questions now. It is possible that we will learn things about the moon and/or the space environment which will make extended habitation of space biologically, technologically or economically unfeasible. However, that appears most unlikely in terms of our present knowledge. In fact, the indications are just the opposite. Life in space will be easier, cheaper, safer and more pleasant than generally realized.

Many people, including some well-known scientists, believe

264

that it is too early to come to any conclusions about space colonies —we have too little information to make intelligent decisions—and that we should withhold judgment on these questions until after we have made our exploratory trips.

Withholding judgment or postponing decision is often the wise and mature course on questions of philosophy and science where the evidence is indecisive and where no decision is urgently required. However, the businessman, the military commander and the gamesman often finds himself forced by necessity to make decisions on the basis of such inadequate data that his decision making is little better than guess work. However, by applying certain general rules and his knowledge of similar past situations, the skillful gamesman can raise his probability of success well above pure chance. An army commander may capture high ground even before he has made any specific plans for its tactical employment. An entrepreneur may buy up goods that are in short supply even without a plan for marketing them.

Likewise, the space-age strategist may see the necessity for making decisions about the future developments of space flight even though data is insufficient for final proof of feasibility.

THE PANAMA THEORY

In this context, an astropolitical theory was proposed by one of the authors, the Panama theory, which can be stated, "There are strategic areas in space—vital to future scientific, commercial and military space programs—which could be excluded from our use through occupation and control by unfriendly powers, unless first occupied by the nations of the free world." This is called the Panama theory in analogy with the strategically significant Panama Canal, since it is believed that some areas in space will come to have this same kind of importance in future interplanetary operations.

Some possible areas are the poles of the moon (because of the possibility of finding water there), the earth-moon libration points (such as the zero gravity point between earth and moon) and perhaps some of the asteroids.

There are five libration or oscillation points about the moon. They lie 60° ahead of and behind the moon in its orbit and also 180° ahead. Two others are on the earth-moon line—one on the near side at about 30,000 miles from the moon and one beyond the moon.

All of these are equilibrium points for an orbiting object, but some represent stable and some unstable equilibria. The three with the most strategic significance are those 60° ahead and behind the moon and the cislunar point (between earth and moon). Of these the first two are stable and the third is unstable. All three of these points could be very useful for refueling and resupply for many types of deep-space vehicles including lunar, interplanetary and military scout and task force vehicles. Occupation of these points by one space power could preclude their use by any other nation which arrived on the scene too late to stake any claims.

Some of the asteroids could have strategic significance in the long-range picture because of the possibility of displacing them from their orbits for either military or commercial purposes. The possibilities for using certain asteroids for interplanetary bases or even capturing them in earth orbits have been discussed previously by the authors.* These possibilities obviously imply a strategic significance to these tiny, deep-space objects. Occupation of some of the close approaching group by an unfriendly power would be a matter for concern.

The possible commercial use of this close-approach group of asteroids should be carefully noted. Some of the very small ones could be diverted from their orbits and brought in to satellite orbits about the earth. They would then serve as sources of raw materials for propellants, structural materials for space ships, etc. Thus a nation in control of these bodies could gain an enormous advantage in the conquest and eventual colonization of space.

The moon itself, because of its low gravity and its store of raw

---

* I. M. Levitt, "Hitch Hiking On An Asteroid," *Newark Sunday News*, Oct. 16, 1961 and D. M. Cole, *Strategic Areas In Space—The Panama Theory* (Los Angeles: Institute of Aerospace Sciences), March 15, 1962.

materials, could prove to be a "Panama Canal" to the riches of the deep space "Pacific Ocean" beyond.

A propellant manufacturer with a production facility on the moon would have an enormous advantage over any earth-based competitor in resupplying interplanetary vehicles. His tankers would have to expend only about one-twentieth the energy in carrying their cargoes to escape velocity as earth-based vehicles would expend for the same mission. Where a four-stage, chemical vehicle might be employed by the earth supplier, the moon-based tanker could be the equivalent of only the fourth and smallest stage of the earth vehicle.

Fig. 21-1   The inner solar system showing orbits of some close-approach asteroids.

Illus.: General Electric—MSD

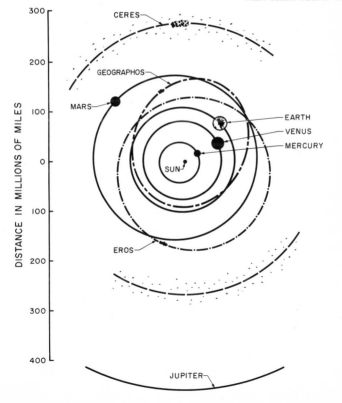

Of course, this comparison might not be relevant if lunar construction and maintenance costs remained prohibitively high because of earth-moon transportation costs. Thus the energy advantage might be outweighed. For the early day of lunar operation this will doubtless be true, and extensive industrial operations will be impossible for the first moon colonists, just as the early settlers in the western hemisphere could not have built and operated a Panama Canal. It was easier for them to sail all the way around Cape Horn. But the day will come when the lunar colony can manufacture propellants—first for use by returning moon-earth vehicles and, eventually, for the use of the interplanetary ships on their long trips to Mars, Venus, Mercury, the asteroids and the satellites of the major planets.

REQUIREMENTS FOR LIFE IN SPACE

It was seen earlier (Chapter 20) that life can exist only within narrow bands of temperature, atmospheric pressure and oxygen percentage in the atmosphere. It was also stated that life must have large supplies of liquid water readily available in order to survive and grow. However, note that this is *unprotected life*. Suppose that we send capsules to the moon or into deep space containing life that is protected from the rigors of the natural environment and containing all the supplies needed for the trip. What are the basic and unchanging requirements for these supplies and how long would they last? How long could the trip continue? New students of astrobiology or exobiology may be surprised to find out that it is not fundamentally necessary that the material supplies ever run out—the space capsule, if properly designed and equipped, can support life forever or for as long as it is supplied with energy.

The earth is a gigantic space capsule. It carries us through space at 18 miles per second on its journey around the sun. We are protected from the rigors of the natural environment of space by the earth's magnetic field and by our heavy blanket of air—about 2000 pounds for every square foot of the earth's surface. The earth is a closed and balanced ecological * system that has supported life for billions of years and can continue to do so as long as its supply of energy is continued.

As any student of biology knows, plants use carbon dioxide and water plus the energy of sunlight to produce oxygen and many food and structural compounds. As long as they have the necessary sunlight, carbon dioxide and water, plus small amounts of other chemicals provided by animal waste products, they can live and grow.

Animals need oxygen, water and the foods produced by plants in order to sustain life. Thus it turns out that all the necessary life chemicals can be passed back and forth between the plants and animals forever, or as long as energy is supplied to keep this great biological cycle turning.

The picture on earth is not quite as simple as described above. For example, large amounts of carbon dioxide captured by shell fish are used in producing calcium carbonate shells which may eventually become limestone. The carbon dioxide can then be unlocked only by great heat or by the action of acids. In contrast, carbon dioxide in the atmosphere may lose oxygen through the action of high-energy solar radiation.

Thus the cycle is not necessarily in perfect balance and proportions of the principal ingredients may change gradually. It is thought, for example, that the percentage of carbon dioxide in the atmosphere has increased since the beginning of the Industrial Revolution because of the combustion of the enormous quantities of fuel required to heat our homes and power our factories and vehicles. However, it is not fundamental to this discussion whether the earth's ecological cycle is perfectly balanced or not. In theory it could be, or could be made so with a little human planning and control.

* Ecology—dealing with the mutual relations between organisms and their environment.

In theory, also, such a closed and balanced ecological system can be made on a much smaller scale, and we can actually build small models of our own natural, earth-space colony.

Projects are now under way at several government and industrial facilities to duplicate the earth on a small scale in space simulators or lunar base simulators. These structures will measure only 30 to 50 feet across but will house enough plants, animals and men to provide an approximate ecological balance. Actually, of course, perfection cannot be expected and reservoirs or "banks" of essential materials will be required. Thus materials which are

Fig. 21-2 A possible early experimental closed and balanced ecological system.

Illus.: General Electric—MSD

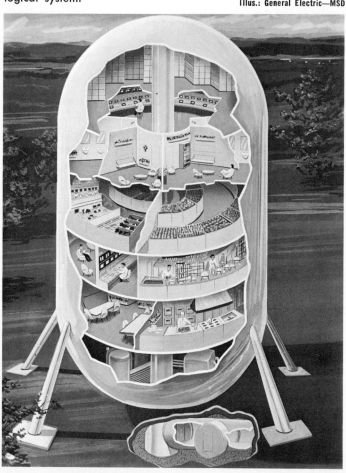

overproduced will be "deposited" in the "bank" and "withdrawn" later on when needed.

When such balanced systems have been developed to a satisfactory state and the propulsion systems are available to carry them into space, men will finally be independent of their home planet and able to cruise for indefinitely long periods through the solar system.

It is possible that these closed ecological systems will never be perfectly balanced. The "bank" required for an earth-moon ship would probably be larger than the supply of oxygen, etc. needed for the trip and, thus, the "natural" system would not be used. On the moon itself the supplies of the closed system will probably be supplemented from lunar materials, particularly when the colonies begin to grow. Thus, again, it will not be a theoretically perfect balance.

Perhaps the closest approaches to the true, balanced systems will be on the interplanetary vehicles on trips of several years duration. For these ships the material stored in the "bank" may only be a small percentage of the total needed for an unrecycled trip.

With a sufficiently tough and durable shell, a supply of raw materials, a continuing supply of energy and the necessary knowledge or training to properly manipulate the energy and materials, a colony of life forms can live and grow anywhere in the universe except in areas so close to stars that the protective qualities of their shells are overloaded. Also, a colony must stay close enough to a star to receive its required energy input, unless it utilizes stored reserves of nuclear materials for its energy supply.

This concept of the enclosed and protected ecological system leads to an ecosphere much larger than that proposed by Strughold (Chapter 20). Without assuming the use of stored energy, this encapsulated life could thrive throughout most of our solar system, from inside the orbit of Mercury to beyond the orbits of Jupiter and Saturn.

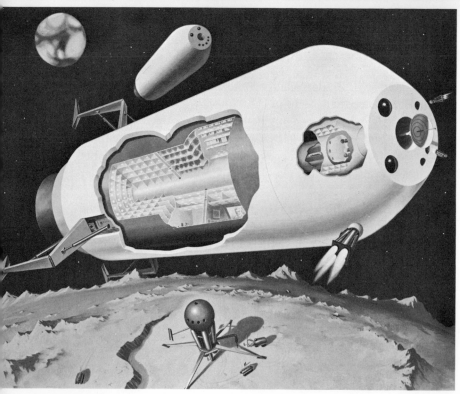

Fig. 21-3 Macro-life unit taking on supplies of raw material on an asteroid.

Illus.: General Electric—MSD

Capsules near the sun would need heavy walls for protection against the solar radiation. Beyond about two astronomical units from the sun, reflectors or solar-energy collectors would be required to increase the input of energy. The limit to the distance at which a colony could thrive on solar energy would depend on the feasible limit of collector size. Thus a new concept of the ecosphere can be stated when we include the assumptions of protection and high degree of organization of the life forms.

It has been suggested by one of the authors and by Dr. Isaac Asimov that the highly organized and protected (encapsulated) concentration of living matter discussed above represents the next step in evolution beyond multicelled life. This new life form has been called "Macro-life" (Cole) and "multi-organismic life" (Asimov).

The major steps in the organization of matter from the creation of the universe until the present can be listed as follows:

1) Energy

2) Subatomic particles

3) Atoms

Fig. 21-4 A Macro-life unit on one of the moons of Mars.

Illus.: Martin Company

4) Molecules

5) Unicellular life

6) Multicellular life

7) Macro-life

Macro-life is characterized by a high degree of organization of its component organisms (comparable to the organization of the organs of the human body), an integration of anabolic and catabolic forms (plants and animals) and a complete independence from any effect of its external environment other than its energy supply.

The concept of Macro-life then creates the need for a new definition of the ecosphere and an extension of its boundaries to in-

Fig. 21-5 A moon colony.

Illus.: General Electric—MSD

Fig. 21-6 The lunar pleasure dome. The exercise and recreation area of a lunar colony. Note that the low gravity of the moon would permit muscle powered flight and other unusual physical activities.

Illus.: Martin Company

clude the entire region of possible habitation of this protected and highly organized life. To distinguish this new concept from the ecosphere of Strughold which assumes unprotected life, the term *Macrosphere* is suggested. The Macrosphere is the volume of space about a star in which Macro-life could exist on a continuous basis without depleting supplies of stored energy.

Although the physical details of the construction of independent, Macro-life units will not be considered here, it should be noted that they could range in size from colonies of perhaps 5000 people in Queen Mary-sized space ships to colonies of millions of people on asteroids, satellites or planets. Perhaps the most perfect example of Macro-life, however, would be the colony in a hollow asteroid with the capability for motion (by rocket propulsion) and reproduction (through expansion of its human, plant and animal

Fig. 21-7 A colony in a lunar cave.

populations and construction of a new unit by hollowing out a second asteroid). This process could go on indefinitely as long as the supply of raw materials in the solar system lasted.

Colonies in hollow asteroids could even embark on interstellar trips lasting hundreds or thousands of years and discover complete new solar systems for colonization. This concept of the "Space Ark," proposed by Dr. Leslie R. Shepard, was enlarged upon by one of the authors to include the concept of a "pastoral" or "natural" world. It was suggested that if the inhabitants of such hollow asteroids were to spend their entire lives on them, an earth-like countryside might be preferable to a ship-like interior structure. Rather than living in a completely filled and structured interior the inhabitants might prefer a random arrangement of brooks, fields, forests, villages, etc. Such a setting could actually be constructed on the inner wall of a large hollowed-out asteroid, although the expense would obviously exceed that of the fully structured interior.

NON-HUMAN LIFE IN SPACE

An interesting question arises from the description of Macro-life and the Macrosphere in the last section. It concerns the importance of human intelligence to the creation and perpetuation of the Macro-life creature. As pictured above, Macro-life units would be constructed, populated and maintained by human beings. This appears to be the direction of evolution on earth, with human intelligence a necessary ingredient. Actually, however, it would be theoretically possible to train animals to carry on the routine maintenance functions of the unit. In fact, animals could be bred that would perform these functions as a result of heriditary behavior patterns (instincts). So the question arises, "Could such a system develop naturally through a process of evolution without the intervention of human intelligence at all?" Presumably it could—at least theoretically. It would not be necessary for the outer shell or *exoskeleton* to be made of metal. Bone, shell, tusk, tooth, claw or

Fig. 21-8 A cutaway showing the inside of a hollowed-out asteroid.

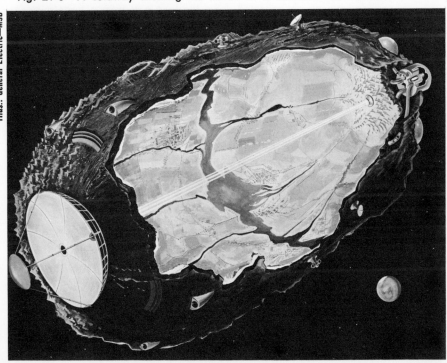

Illus.: General Electric—MSD

Fig. 21-9. Hollow asteroid from the inside. Artificial gravity is provided by spinning the asteroid about its long axis. Light and heat are provided by sunlight reflected down the long axis from a large mirror.

antler-type materials would serve just as well. Thus there is no great theoretical stumbling block in so far as the protective covering is concerned. Snails, lobsters, turtles and clams are examples of types of encapsulated life which could perhaps survive the rigors of the lunar environment. (Not these earth animals, but similar forms.) Now, what about the animal and vegetable combination? Many forms of highly integrated symbiosis between plants and animals are known on earth—the complete integration into one organism does not seem impossible for an extra-terrestrial life form.

As described in the previous chapter, current theories on exolife are based on the concept of "life as we know it." This is life based on the organic chemistry of the carbon atom and, more particularly, on the self replicating (or reproducing) properties of the

DNA (desoxyribonucleic acid) molecule. Although life forms based on silicon rather than carbon have been proposed, such forms seem unlikely because of the intrinsically greater suitability of carbon as the basic life element. This inherent capability of carbon is not simply a function of its unique atomic structure and consequent position at the center and the top of the periodic table. Silicon simply does not have the atomic structure permitting the widely versatile combinations which are uniquely characteristic of carbon. Although silicon life may be possible under certain conditions, it does not seem very probable.

Two other tacit assumptions are included in current reasoning on exolife: that it is unprotected and that it is below the level of organization which would permit a stable, symbiotic equilibrium between anabolic and catabolic forms. Since such forms cannot be excluded on fundamental, theoretical grounds, we may question whether the rigid, current, application of the "life as we know it" approach is the most useful picture of the as yet largely unknown biocosmos. The encapsulated, stable, symbiotic form, while still within the framework of carbon-based and even DNA-based life, greatly extends the exosphere about a star. The new Macrosphere for the solar system then must include the planets, the satellites and the asteroids with the possible exceptions only of the outermost planets because of the low energy supply.

No distinction is made here between the natural and artificial Macrospheres, that is, the habitat of naturally evolving, encapsulated, symbiotic life as compared to that of the man-made and man-maintained forms. Both could theoretically exist throughout the solar system.

Whereas man-made forms would require large solar collectors when operating at more than two or three astronomical units from the sun, non-human forms could use a "battery-charging," dormancy-dynamic cycle to replace the large collectors. While energy collection and storage would take place constantly, energy expenditure (in growth and motion) would be limited to short periods, with most of the total life span spent in a dormant state.

The high gravity of Jupiter would be a severe handicap for the human, Macro-life units, although men would probably eventually learn to tolerate even the Jovian surface gravity. However, this should not be a problem for the naturally evolving form. Thus none of the bodies in the solar system except the sun itself can be ruled out on basic, theoretical grounds as either future homesites for men or present homesites for non-human, encapsulated, symbiotes.

The most serious objection that may be raised to this suggestion is not in connection with the present ability of such a life form to exist almost anywhere in the solar system (which cannot be seriously challenged in view of our own plans to travel extensively in interplanetary space) but in the possibility of such organisms evolving under any but the limited conditions of the Strughold ecosphere. This objection would be the most serious in connection with the asteroids and small satellites because of the absence of liquid water. On the moon and the large satellites, however, liquid water could occur beneath the surface, and on the planets liquefied gases might serve some of the same purposes as water in the evolutionary process.

It may not be worthwhile to spend much time developing general laws of exobiology at this time, since the present evidence is so meager and since we can expect so much significant data in the very near future. However, we should note the *major logical difference* in statements of the type, "a perpetual motion machine of the first class cannot operate because such operation would contradict the law of conservation of energy," and the statement, "life could not evolve or persist on Mercury, Jupiter or the moon, because they are not included in the Strughold ecosphere."

Probably the most exciting aspect of our space program and of our future in space is that we just do not know what we will find when we set foot on a new world in space.

The Payload
Performance Equation

ROCKET AND SPACE vehicle performance is commonly discussed in the literature in terms of the burn-out velocity of the empty rocket. Use of empty rocket mass as a basic parameter has the disadvantage that the payload mass is not specified, and thus the true payload performance cannot be determined. A less common, but more instructive method of analysis uses the gross-to-payload ratio and finds the dependence of this ratio on the fundamental rocket performance parameters.

The most basic of the rocket performance parameters are: the two-mission requirements, *mission velocity* and *gross-to-payload ratio,* and the two rocket parameters which together must provide this mission performance, that is, the *effective exhaust velocity* and the *propellant fraction.* A simple algebraic expression can be derived which relates these four parameters. This expression can be written as

$$\frac{G}{L} = \frac{F}{e^{-v/c} + F - 1} \qquad (1)$$

where G = gross or take-off mass
L = payload mass

$v =$ mission velocity or velocity change
$c =$ effective exhaust velocity $= KgI_{sp}$
$I_{sp} =$ ideal vacuum specific impulse
$K =$ all losses due to atmosphere and gravity
$g =$ dimensionless constant numerically equal to the acceleration of gravity at sea level and $45°$ north latitude

$F =$ propellant fraction $= \dfrac{P}{G - L}$
$P =$ propellant mass

This expression can be derived from the basic rocket equation of motion as follows. From Newton's second law of motion the rocket thrust, T, is related to the instantaneous rocket mass, M, and the rocket acceleration, a, by

$$T = Ma \qquad (2)$$

Also, the thrust is related to the exhaust *velocity*, c, and propellant mass flow rate, $\dot{m}$, by

$$T = -\dot{m}c = -c\frac{dm}{dt} \qquad (3)$$

where (3) has also been derived from the second law. The rocket thrust is equal to the rate of change of momentum of the exhaust which is $d(mc)/dt$. Since c is assumed to be constant, this equals $c(dm/dt)$.

Then from (2) and (3),

$$M\frac{dv}{dt} = -c\frac{dm}{dt} \qquad (4)$$

since

$$a = \frac{dv}{dt}$$

Then

$$dv = -c\frac{dm}{M} \quad \text{or} \quad v = -c\int \cdot \frac{dm}{M} \qquad (5)$$

Now, if v is the change in velocity in the interval, during which the mass changes from M_1 to M_2,

$$v \Big|_{M_1}^{M_2} = -c \int \frac{M_2\, dm}{M_1} = -c\, \frac{dm}{M} = c \ln M \Big|_{M_2}^{M_1}$$

and

$$v = c \ln \frac{M_1}{M_2} \tag{6}$$

Now let $M_1 = G$ and $M_2 = E$, where E equals empty weight, that is, $(S + L)$, where S is the hardware weight not counted as payload.

Now, from (6),

$$\frac{M_1}{M_2} = \frac{G}{E} = e^{v/c} \tag{7}$$

and the reciprocal form

$$\frac{E}{G} = e^{-v/c} \tag{8}$$

However, note that

$$E = (G - P) = G - F(G - L) \tag{9}$$

Then, from (8) and (9),

$$\frac{G - F(G - L)}{G} = e^{-v/c} \tag{10}$$

and

$$1 - F + \frac{FL}{G} = e^{-v/c} \tag{11}$$

Thus

$$\frac{FL}{G} = e^{-v/c} + F - 1 \tag{12}$$

and dividing both sides by F we have the payload fraction,

$$\frac{L}{G} = \frac{e^{-v/c} + F - 1}{F} \tag{13}$$

Finally,

$$\frac{G}{L} = \frac{F}{e^{-v/c} + F - 1}$$

This useful relation can also be expressed as

$$c = \frac{v}{\ln (G/L) - \ln [G/L - F(G/L - 1)]} \qquad (14)$$

or

$$F = \frac{G/L(1 - e^{-v/c})}{(G/L) - 1} \qquad (15)$$

according to the reader's preference, availability of tables, etc.

As an example of the use of Equation (14), assume that a one-stage, lunar landing vehicle ($v = 45,000$ feet per second) is required with a G/L of 10. Find the combinations of c or I_{sp} and F which will provide this performance.

Then

$$c = \frac{45,000}{2.30 - \ln [10 - 9F]}$$

Five operations are required to find each value of c corresponding to a value of F. Using Equation (15),

$$F = 1.11 [1 - e^{-45,000/c}]$$

which requires only four operations and which is preferable if good tables of e^{-x} are available. For parametric studies, values of c can be chosen such that values of x will correspond to those in whatever tables one has at hand.

Note that a Rover-type nuclear vehicle which could deliver an average effective c of 22,500 feet per second ($I_{sp} = 700$ stapps) after all losses had been subtracted, could satisfy the mission requirements above if an F of 0.96 could be achieved. Although $F = 0.96$ is not out of the question for large chemical rockets using propellants of average density, it seems unlikely for nuclear rockets using liquid hydrogen expellant.

At a more conservative value of F of 0.84, the propulsion system would have to average 32,200 feet per second or an I_{sp} of 1000. This is not an unreasonable average figure since I_{sp} values of 1200 can probably be achieved for all but the first 15,000 feet per second velocity change.

Powers of *e*

Exponentials (e^n and e^{-n}).

n	e^n	Diff.	n	e^n	Diff.	n	e^n	n	e^{-n}	Diff.	n	e^{-n}	n	e^{-n}
0.00	1.000	10	0.50	1.649	16	1.0	2.718*	0.00	1.000—10		0.50	.607	1.0	.368*
.01	1.010	10	.51	1.665	17	.1	3.004	.01	0.990—10		.51	.600	.1	.333
.02	1.020	10	.52	1.682	17	.2	3.320	.02	.980—10		.52	.595	.2	.301
.03	1.030	11	.53	1.699	17	.3	3.669	.03	.970— 9		.53	.589	.3	.273
.04	1.041	10	.54	1.716	17	.4	4.055	.04	.961—10		.54	.583	.4	.247
0.05	1.051	11	0.55	1.733	18	1.5	4.482	0.05	.951— 9		0.55	.577	1.5	.223
.06	1.062	11	.56	1.751	17	.6	4.953	.06	.942—10		.56	.571	.6	.202
.07	1.073	10	.57	1.768	18	.7	5.474	.07	.932— 9		.57	.566	.7	.183
.08	1.083	11	.58	1.786	18	.8	6.050	.08	.923— 9		.58	.560	.8	.165
.09	1.094	11	.59	1.804	18	.9	6.686	.09	.914— 9		.59	.554	.9	.150
0.10	1.105	11	0.60	1.822	18	2.0	7.389	0.10	.905— 9		0.60	.549	2.0	.135
.11	1.116	11	.61	1.840	19	.1	8.166	.11	.896— 9		.61	.543	.1	.122
.12	1.127	12	.62	1.859	19	.2	9.025	.12	.887— 9		.62	.538	.2	.111
.13	1.139	11	.63	1.878	18	.3	9.974	.13	.878— 9		.63	.533	.3	.100
.14	1.150	12	.64	1.896	20	.4	11.02	.14	.869— 8		.64	.527	.4	.0907
0.15	1.162	12	0.65	1.916	19	2.5	12.18	0.15	.861— 9		0.65	.522	2.5	.0821
.16	1.174	11	.66	1.935	19	.6	13.46	.16	.852— 8		.66	.517	.6	.0743
.17	1.185	12	.67	1.954	20	.7	14.88	.17	.844— 9		.67	.512	.7	.0672
.18	1.197	12	.68	1.974	20	.8	16.44	.18	.835— 8		.68	.507	.8	.0608
.19	1.209	12	.69	1.994	20	.9	18.17	.19	.827— 8		.69	.502	.9	.0550
0.20	1.221	13	0.70	2.014	20	3.0	20.09	0.20	.819— 8		0.70	.497	3.0	.0498
.21	1.234	12	.71	2.034	20	.1	22.20	.21	.811— 8		.71	.492	.1	.0450
.22	1.246	13	.72	2.054	21	.2	24.53	.22	.803— 8		.72	.487	.2	.0408
.23	1.259	12	.73	2.075	21	.3	27.11	.23	.795— 8		.73	.482	.3	.0369
.24	1.271	13	.74	2.096	21	.4	29.96	.24	.787— 8		.74	.477	.4	.0334
0.25	1.284	13	0.75	2.117	21	3.5	33.12	0.25	.779— 8		0.75	.472	3.5	.0302
.26	1.297	13	.76	2.138	22	.6	36.60	.26	.771— 8		.76	.468	.6	.0273
.27	1.310	13	.77	2.160	21	.7	40.45	.27	.763— 7		.77	.463	.7	.0247
.28	1.323	13	.78	2.181	22	.8	44.70	.28	.756— 8		.78	.458	.8	.0224
.29	1.336	14	.79	2.203	23	.9	49.40	.29	.748— 7		.79	.454	.9	.0202
0.30	1.350	13	0.80	2.226	22	4.0	54.60	0.30	.741— 8		0.80	.449	4.0	.0183
.31	1.363	14	.81	2.248	22	.1	60.34	.31	.733— 7		.81	.445	.1	.0166
.32	1.377	14	.82	2.270	23	.2	66.69	.32	.726— 7		.82	.440	.2	.0150
.33	1.391	14	.83	2.293	23	.3	73.70	.33	.719— 7		.83	.436	.3	.0136
.34	1.405	14	.84	2.316	24	.4	81.45	.34	.712— 7		.84	.432	.4	.0123

Exponentials (e^n and e^{-n}).

n	e^n	Diff.	n	e^n	Diff.	n	e^{-n}	n	e^n	Diff.	n	e^{-n}	n	e^{-n}
0.35	1.419	14	0.85	2.340	23	4.5	90.02	0.35	.705—	7	0.85	.427	4.5	.0111
.36	1.433	15	.86	2.363	24			.36	.698—	7	.86	.423		
.37	1.448	14	.87	2.387	24	5.0	148.4	.37	.691—	7	.87	.419	5.0	.00674
.38	1.462	15	.88	2.411	24	6.0	403.4	.38	.684—	7	.88	.415	6.0	.00248
.39	1.477	15	.89	2.435	25	7.0	1097.	.39	.677—	7	.89	.411	7.0	.000912
0.40	1.492	15	0.90	2.460	24	8.0	2981.	0.40	.670—	6	0.90	.407	8.0	.000335
.41	1.507	15	.91	2.484	25	9.0	8103.	.41	.664—	7	.91	.403	9.0	.000123
.42	1.522	15	.92	2.509	26	10.0	22026.	.42	.657—	6	.92	.399	10.0	.000045
.43	1.537	16	.93	2.535	25	$\pi/2$	4.810	.43	.651—	7	.93	.395	$\pi/2$	.208
.44	1.553	15	.94	2.560	26	$2\pi/2$	23.14	.44	.644—	6	.94	.391	$2\pi/2$	.0432
0.45	1.568	16	0.95	2.586	26	$3\pi/2$	111.3	0.45	.638—	7	0.95	.387	$3\pi/2$	.00898
.46	1.584	16	.96	2.612	26	$4\pi/2$	535.5	.46	.631—	6	.96	.383	$4\pi/2$	.00187
.47	1.600	16	.97	2.638	26	$5\pi/2$	2576.	.47	.625—	6	.97	.379	$5\pi/2$	.000388
.48	1.616	16	.98	2.664	27	$6\pi/2$	12392.	.48	.619—	6	.98	.375	$6\pi/2$	.000081
.49	1.632	17	.99	2.691	27	$7\pi/2$	59610.	.49	.613—	6	.99	.372	$7\pi/2$	.000017
0.50	1.649		1.00	2.718		$8\pi/2$	286751.	0.50	0.607—		1.00	.368	$8\pi/2$	.000003

* Note 1.—Do not interpolate in this column $e = 2.71828$ $1/e = 0.367879$
$\log_{10} e = 0.4343$ $1/(0.4343) = 2.3026$ $\log_{10} (0.4343) = 1.6378$ $\log_{10} (e^n) = n(0.4343)$
Note 2.—This table was taken from B. O. Pierce, *A Short Table of Integrals,* Ginn and Company.

Satellite Velocity
Requirements

How fast must a rocket go in order to go into orbit? Almost everyone has a ready answer to this question now that we have entered the space age, about 18,000 miles per hour or 26,000 feet per second. Of course, that answer applies only to circular orbits close to the earth.

For close orbits the actual velocity of the satellite in orbit is also, approximately, the burn-out velocity required of the rocket in order to establish the orbit. You may know that for orbits of larger radius the satellite velocity is actually lower until, at the moon's distance, the velocity is only about 3500 feet per second. Then is the rocket velocity required actually less for higher orbits? Of course it is not, since the satellite must be projected to the orbit altitude as well as being supplied with the orbital velocity.

It can easily be shown that the zero-altitude, orbital velocity is

$$S = \sqrt{gR_0}$$

where R_0 is the radius of the earth, since the centrifugal force mS^2/R_0 must equal the weight mg. Thus, $S^2 = gR_0$.

For higher orbits the satellite velocity will decrease with the square root of the radial distance in the form

$$v_c = S\sqrt{\frac{R_0}{R}} = R_0\sqrt{\frac{g}{R}}$$

But this is for circular orbits only and tells us nothing about the more general elliptical case, nor does it answer the question of the required velocity.

It can be shown that the velocity for a satellite on an elliptical orbit varies in a manner similar to the circular orbit, but the velocity changes with position on the orbit. Thus it is necessary to pick a point, such as the apogee or perigee, to specify the velocity. Then we find that *the velocity of a satellite at apogee is equal to the equivalent circular velocity at the apogee distance multiplied by the square root of the perigee ratio.*

The perigee ratio as used here is simply the perigee distance divided by the semi-major axis; thus

$$v_A = v_c\sqrt{P/a}$$

This can also be expressed as

$$v_A = v_c\sqrt{\frac{2P}{A+P}}$$

if we wish to work with apogee and perigee distances only.

Similarly, it can be stated that *the velocity of a satellite at perigee is equal to the equivalent circular velocity at the perigee distance multiplied by the square root of the apogee ratio.*

$$v_P = v_c\sqrt{\frac{A}{a}} = v_c\sqrt{\frac{2A}{A+P}}$$

Now with these equations available we not only have the velocities for key points on elliptical orbits, but we can also determine the actual rocket burn-out velocity requirements. We find these requirements in the following way.

Suppose that we wish to place a satellite in a high, circular orbit with radius R. The velocity of the satellite in this orbit will be, as explained earlier, $v_c = S\sqrt{R_0/R}$, but this is not the velocity required to achieve the orbit.

First the rocket must enter an elliptical orbit with an apogee distance equal to the desired circular-orbit radius. Assume that perigee is equal to the earth's radius. Then the perigee velocity, or burn-out velocity, will be

$$v_P = v_c\sqrt{A/a} = S\sqrt{A/a} = S\sqrt{R/a}$$

Now the satellite will rise to the desired altitude but will not have sufficient velocity when it arrives to remain on the circular orbit. Thus the rocket must fire again and supply the difference between circular and apogee velocity.

Apogee velocity is

$$v_A = v_c\sqrt{R_0/a}$$

which is

$$v_A = S\sqrt{R_0/R}\,\sqrt{R_0/a}$$

Then the difference between circular and apogee velocity is

$$v_c - v_A = S\sqrt{R_0/R} - v_A$$

or

$$S\sqrt{R_0/R}\,[1 - \sqrt{R_0/a}]$$

The total velocity change required, v_t, is then

$$v_c - v_A + v_P = S\sqrt{R_0/R} - S\sqrt{R_0/R}\,\sqrt{R_0/a} + S\sqrt{R/a}$$

or

$$v_t = S\left[\sqrt{\frac{R_0}{R}} - \frac{R_0}{\sqrt{Ra}} + \sqrt{\frac{R}{a}}\right]$$

Suppose, for example, that we pick a circular orbit with a radius equal to 49 earth radii. (Approximately 196,000 miles from the center of the earth.) Note: a represents the semi-major axis of the transfer ellipse.

Then

$$v = S\left[\frac{1}{7} - \frac{1}{35} + \frac{7}{5}\right]$$

$$= S \times \frac{53}{35} = 1.515S = 7.42 \text{ miles per second}$$

Note that this is actually higher than escape velocity from the earth's surface! This remarkable condition arises from the unescapable necessity to fire the rocket engines twice in order to establish a high circular orbit. Thus energy must be expended to raise propellants to the orbit altitude.

Figure A-1 shows circular velocity, required perigee velocity, apogee velocity and total required velocity as functions of orbit radius measured in earth radii. It will be noticed that the total velocity required for placing payloads in circular orbits exceeds escape velocity for orbits with radii greater than about 3.5 earth radii, or about 10,000 miles altitude. The velocity requirement increases to a maximum of 7.56 miles per second at about 16 earth radii and then decreases very gradually to about 7.33 at 100 earth radii and escape velocity at infinity. The figures given are based on an earth radius of 3958.89 miles and a zero-altitude orbit velocity of 4.916 miles per second.

One final equation will be presented which gives the satellite (or planet) velocity at any point on an elliptical orbit.

$$v = \sqrt{GM\left(\frac{2}{R} - \frac{1}{a}\right)} = R_0 \sqrt{g\left(\frac{2}{R} - \frac{1}{a}\right)}$$

where G is the universal constant of gravity and M is the mass of the primary. Note that $GM = gR_0^2$ for the earth, since the force of gravity on a mass, m, at the earth's surface is equal to its weight.

$$F = \frac{GMm}{R_0^2} = mg$$

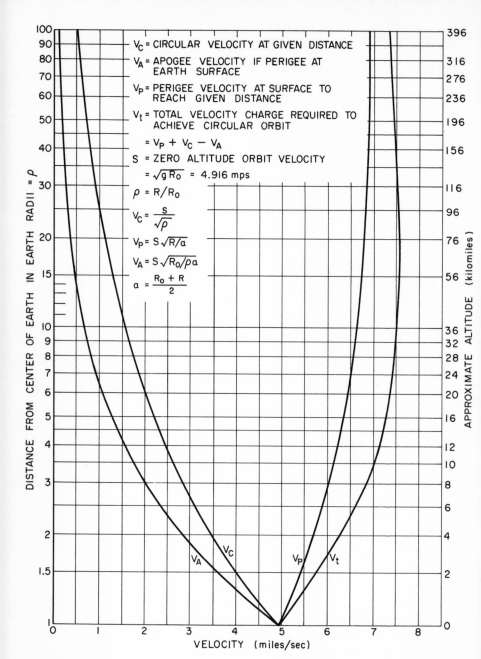

Fig. A-1 Satellite velocity requirements.

Derivation of the Law of Gravity from Kepler's Third Law

K EPLER'S THIRD LAW of planetary motion can be written as

$$\frac{P_1^2}{P_2^2} = \frac{R_1^3}{R_2^3}$$

where P_1 and R_1 are the period and the radial distance from planet (1) to the sun and P_2 and R_2 refer to a second planet. Thus "the squares of the periods of any two planets are in the same proportion as the cubes of their mean distances from the sun."

This law can be rewritten for circular orbits in terms of the orbital velocity of the planets rather than their periods.

Thus the velocity of a planet in its orbit is $v = C/P$, where $C = 2\pi R$ is the circumference of the orbit.

Then

$$P = \frac{2\pi R}{v}$$

and the third law is

$$\frac{(2\pi R_1)^2}{v_1^2} \div \frac{(2\pi R_2)^2}{v_2^2} = \frac{R_1^3}{R_2^3}$$

293

or

$$\frac{R_1{}^2}{v_1{}^2} \times \frac{v_2{}^2}{R_2{}^2} = \frac{R_1{}^3}{R_2{}^3}$$

and

$$\frac{v_2{}^2}{v_1{}^2} = \frac{R_1}{R_2}$$

and, finally,

$$v_1{}^2 R_1 = v_2{}^2 R_2 = v_3{}^2 R_3 = \text{a constant}$$

Thus, a corollary of Kepler's third law for circular orbits is that the radii of the planets are inversely proportional to the squares of their velocities. This is a useful relation in determining the approximate orbital velocities of the other planets in terms of the earth's known velocity and distance from the sun.

An important law of dynamics which can be derived entirely apart from planetary motion and which applies to all curvilinear motion is that the centripetal force acting on an object is inversely proportional to the radius of curvature and directly proportional to the product of the mass of the object and the square of its velocity. This can be written as

$$F = \frac{mv^2}{R}$$

Now it is interesting to note that the centripetal force acting on a planet in a circular orbit is proportional to the square of its velocity, which we know from the corollary to Kepler's third law to be inversely proportional to its radial distance from the sun. That is,

$$v_1{}^2 R_1 = k \quad \text{or} \quad v_1{}^2 = \frac{k}{R_1}$$

Now, if this is substituted in the formula for centripetal force,

$$F = \frac{m_1 v_1{}^2}{R_1} = \frac{m_1 k}{R_1{}^2}$$

or "the force accelerating a planet toward the sun is proportional to the mass of the planet and inversely proportional to the square of the distance from the planet to the sun."

This is not quite Newton's law of gravity but it is very close. What is the difference? You probably know that the mass of the sun should also appear in the equation and that the force of gravity between any two objects is "directly proportional to the product of their masses. . . ." Thus

$$F = K \frac{mM}{R^2}$$

The constant, K, is referred to as the universal constant of gravity and is usually represented by the letter, G. It is defined as the force of attraction between two unit masses at unit distance apart and in the CGS system is equal to 6.673×10^{-8} (two one-gram masses one centimeter apart).

It might have been deduced from Newton's third law that the mass of the sun would also have to appear in the expression for the force of gravity (since the force with which the sun was attracted toward the planet would have to equal the force with which the planet was attracted toward he sun).

However, Newton himself, was not satisfied with his derivation of the law of gravity until he had checked it on the earth-moon system. Unfortunately, the estimated value for the distance to the moon which Newton used was so inaccurate that he thought his law must be incorrect. It was not until some 20 years later that a more accurate figure was determined and Newton found that his law of gravity had been right after all.

We have not intended to imply that Newton derived the law of gravity in the simple way used above. He was well aware of the elliptical nature of the planetary orbits and knew that a law of gravity must account for this motion in detail. The full derivation from Kepler's laws assuming elliptical orbits is far too complex to be given here. However, the circular orbit approximation may be of some value in illustrating the relationship between Kepler's laws and the law of gravity. It is at least more likely that a simple derivation of this type led Newton to his historic discovery than that his train of thought was initiated by the fall of an apple!

Derivation
of the Rocket
Flight Equation

U NDERSTANDING OF THE rocket flight equation depends on knowledge of logarithms based on the quantity e. This might all be clear if we knew what e stood for, so perhaps we should spend a few lines on this strange quantity. The letter e is used to represent a somewhat mysterious and fascinating numerical constant called the *base of the natural logarithm* and which has a value of 2.71828+.

The value of e can be worked out to as many decimal places as desired by carrying out the exponential series

$$e = 1 + \frac{1}{1} + \frac{1}{2!} + \frac{1}{3!} + \frac{1}{4!} + \cdots + \frac{1}{n!}$$

where $n!$ stands for n factorial and means $n(n-1)(n-2)$ $(n-3)$. . . . Thus 4! means $4 \times 3 \times 2 \times 1 = 24$, and $5! = 120$.

The number e crops up in many natural relationships and seems to be a fundamental physical constant. For example, it has a function in describing a rectangular hyperbola somewhat analogous to that of π for a circle. A rectangular hyperbola is a special type of hyperbola much as a circle is a special type of ellipse. e is the relationship between a line and an area for the rectangular hyperbola in somewhat the same way that π relates the radius and the area of a circle.

If the distance from the center to the vertex of a rectangular hyperbola is taken as unity, we find that the log of the sum of the x- and y-coordinates of a point on the hyperbola is equal to twice the area under the radius from the center to the point. If this area is taken as unity, $x + y = e$. Also, the increase of the sum of x and y will be logarithmic with time if the areal velocity (the rate at which area is swept out by the radius) is constant.

This geometric and dynamic relationship seems to be closely connected to another basic significance of e; its relationship to what is called *logarithmic growth*.

This fundamental natural law is used by nuclear physicists to predict the future mass of a radioactive element, by market analysts and government planners to predict future population growth, by biologists to predict the increase in numbers of bacteria in a culture and by economists to compute interest on investments.

The law of logarithmic growth is based on the observation that the rate of unrestrained growth of a substance is directly proportional to the amount of the substance present at any time, t. Mathematically, this can be expressed as

$$\frac{dN}{dt} = SN *$$

where $N =$ the number of people, atoms, units of mass, etc.

$S =$ a proportionality constant such as an interest rate of one per cent per year

$t =$ time

This equation can be integrated to give

$$\ln \frac{N}{N_0} = St \quad \text{or} \quad \frac{N}{N_0} = e^{St}$$

---

* Calculus expressions such as this will add to the understanding of those who have studied this branch of mathematics. However, the reader who is not familiar with calculus can, nevertheless, apply the following derived algebraic formulas with confidence, since they have been amply confirmed by experiments.

where N_0 is the value of the quantity at time zero and N is the value at time t. Thus the law of logarithmic growth can be stated as follows: *the natural log of the growth ratio is directly proportional to the growth time.*

If you do not understand what is meant by integration, just accept the equation above as one that can be easily proved by experiments.

Now you will note that this equation is very similar to our basic rocket equation, and we can even consider the special case where $St = 1$ and $N/N_0 = e$. Then the growth ratio or "mass ratio" of the growing population is just equal to 2.72.

Now let us hope that this excursion into the wonders of mathematics has been informative and stimulating and return to the basic rocket flight equation, $v/c = \ln G/E$.

It might be interesting to note that the rocket equation is really a more general case of the growth equation, for which there is no time dependence. Suppose we first look at a special case of the rocket equation in which time is a factor--the constant acceleration rocket.

The thrust of a rocket, T, is equal to the product of the mass flow rate, dm/dt or $\dot{m}$, and the exhaust velocity, c. The thrust is also equal to Ma, where M is the mass of the rocket at any instant and a is its acceleration. Thus the equation can be written,

$$T = Ma = -\dot{m}c$$

with the minus sign inserted since the exhaust velocity is in the opposite direction from the thrust and the vehicle acceleration. Thus

$$\dot{m} = -\frac{Ma}{c} \quad \text{and} \quad \frac{dm}{dt} = -\frac{Ma}{c}$$

or

$$\frac{dm}{M} = -\frac{a}{c}dt$$

Then integration gives

$$\ln \frac{M_1}{M_2} = \frac{a}{c}t \quad \text{or} \quad \ln \frac{G}{E} = \frac{a}{c}t$$

Note that the rate of change of mass, m, or the growth rate, was defined as directly proportional to the mass and that the proportionality constant was a/c. Thus a and c are both constant, or at least the ratio is constant. Then the law of constant acceleration rocket flight is found to be *the burning time of a constant acceleration, constant exhaust velocity rocket is directly proportional to the naural log of the mass ratio.*

This equation can be rewritten as

$$\ln \frac{G}{E} = \frac{T}{Gc}t$$

since $T/G = a$. Of course, the burn-out velocity, v, is equal to at; thus

$$\ln \frac{G}{E} = \frac{v}{c}$$

This is, of course, the first law of rocket flight and is true whether or not the acceleration is constant; thus it is more general than the growth-law form.

Index